THE RUNNER'S WORLD BIG BOOK OF MARATHON and Half-Marathon TRAINING JOURNAL

JENNIFER VAN ALLEN, BART YASSO, AND AMBY BURFOOT
with Pamela Nisevich Bede, RD, CSSD

RODALE.

INTRODUCTION

Running 13.1 or 26.2 miles is no small task, to be sure. But anyone who has done it will tell you that getting to the finish line isn't the tough part—getting to the starting line is.

After all, at most events there are aid stations with food and drink every few miles, scores of cheering spectators offering encouragement, plus the camaraderie of thousands of fellow runners. And at the end, everyone earns a medal for his or her effort.

If only training was that luxurious.

Indeed, race preparation is where the biggest challenge lies. It entails figuring out how to drive your body and mind further than they've ever gone before, without burning out in the process. It demands pushing yourself through hours on the road, often solo, fueled only by your own determination to cover the miles for the day and the faith that you can do it. It requires figuring out which discomforts you can grit your teeth through and which pains demand surrender. It involves committing to the goal every day for hundreds of days before the event, even when the chaos of your own life, or your own self-doubt, makes it extremely tempting to give up.

To be sure, it's on this long, sweaty journey to the starting line that the true personal transformation takes place. This is where individuals morph into athletes, with the gear, training logs, and war wounds that go along with that; it's where dreamers become doers.

In this journal, you'll find everything you need to kick off your training on the right foot and to successfully make it to the starting line. You'll learn how to find a race that's appropriate for you, pick a goal that's realistic, and determine the best strategy to follow to accomplish that goal. You'll learn the basic principles of training, find out what to wear, and get tips on how to juggle the demands of training with the work, family, and social commitments of everyday life.

Master the techniques we give you here, and the race itself will become a victory lap for all of the hundreds of miles you logged, the countless sacrifices you made, and the physical and emotional transformation that took place along the way.

GETTING STARTED

Ready or Not? Before you jump into marathon or half-marathon training, it's important to honestly assess whether you're ready. If you've never run a step before or you're just starting out, jumping into a 25-mile-a-week training program is a surefire way to end up burned-out or hurt.

That is not to say that you have to wait until you reach some ideal weight, or you get perfect running weather, or you get some stress-free 4-month chunk of time at work, the kids are self-sufficient, and you have so much free time that you can train whenever you want, as much as you want. (That day will likely *never* arrive.)

But by taking a few critical steps before you start training for a big race, you'll save yourself a lot of time, hurt, and heartache down the road. Here's what to do before you get started.

Build a Base. As long as you've been running at least four times a week for about 6 months and you're in the habit of exercising regularly, you should be able to complete a marathon or half-marathon training program without a problem. If you haven't been training that consistently, don't fret. You can still run a marathon or half-marathon in the near future. Pick a date one year away, and work your way up to it.

Time It Right. Marathon and half-marathon training are time-consuming, there's no question about it. Plan ahead for any conflicts; figure out which workouts need to be rearranged and which parts of your usual routine will need to be adjusted. Set these plans in motion before you start training. That way, as the runs get longer and the race draws nearer, you won't have the added pressure of trying to figure out how you'll fit it all in.

Assess Your Stress. While running can be a great stress relief, trying to train for a race—especially your first—while contending with other big life changes, like a new baby or a cross-country move, can be a bit much. Only you can decide whether training would reduce or increase your stress.

See the Doctor. It's best to get a checkup before you start training, especially if you're coping with injuries or if you have any family history of heart attack, diabetes, or other chronic illnesses. Visit your doctor right away if you experience chest pain, feelings of pressure, shortness of breath, or some other abnormal sensations while exercising.

Choose the Right Race

Use this checklist when you're comparing different races. Consider each of these factors to figure out which marathon or half-marathon is right for you.

RACE	1	2	3
RACE DATE			
WEEKS TO TRAIN			
LOCATION			
NUMBER OF RUNNERS			
TYPICAL WEATHER CONDITIONS (AVERAGE TEMPERATURE ON RACE DAY)			
HILLY OR FLAT?			
COURSE TIME LIMIT			
MUSIC FRIENDLY			

Picking a Training Plan

The most important thing is that your plan feels doable. The first few weeks should be a natural extension of the running routine that you've already been maintaining. If the plan is a good fit, you'll finish most workouts feeling challenged and exhilarated—like you put in a good, honest effort—but not demolished. But if the plan is too hard for your current level of fitness, you'll go home feeling frustrated and possibly hurt.

If you're a beginner, pick a plan that includes rest days and running days. That plan will give you the most opportunity to practice running and develop the endurance you need with the least risk of injury.

Setting Smart Race Goals

Runners tend to measure success by the minute. But focusing your sights only on a single time can set you up for failure. Miss your mark after all your hard training, and it's such a downer that you may end up quitting. That is not to say that it's impossible to qualify for Boston or break 4:00 on your first try. But setting multiple goals—and making sure that at least one is not defined by the clock—will guarantee a sense of accomplishment come race day, no matter what happens.

How Fast Can You Go?

You can use the finishing time of shorter races to predict your pace for a longer distance.

5-K	10-K	HALF-MARATHON	MARATHON
17:13	35:54	1:19	2:45
17:44	36:59	1:21	2:50
18:16	38:04	1:24	2:55
18:47	39:10	1:26	3:00
19:18	40:15	1:28	3:05
19:50	41:20	1:31	3:10
20:21	42:25	1:33	3:15
20:52	43:31	1:36	3:20
21:23	44:36	1:38	3:25
21:55	45:41	1:40	3:30
22:26	46:46	1:43	3:35
22:57	47:52	1:45	3:40
23:29	48:57	1:48	3:45
24:31	51:08	1:52	3:55
25:03	52:13	1:55	4:00
26:05	54:23	2:00	4:10
26:37	55:29	2:02	4:15
27:39	57:39	2:07	4:25
28:10	58:44	2:09	4:30
29:13	1:01	2:14	4:40
29:44	1:02	2:16	4:45
30:47	1:04	2:21	(4:55)
31:18	1:05	2:24	5:00
32:32	1:07	2:28	5:10
32:52	1:08	2:31	5:15
33:55	1:10	2:35	5:25
34:26	1:11	2:38	5:30

11:15 pace (handwritten annotation)

Source: Runnersworld.com/trainingcalculator

PART 1
TRAINING

We hear from a lot of runners who decide to run a marathon or half-marathon and just go out and run as much as they can, as far as they can, and as fast as they can. You do have to push beyond your limits when you're preparing to run long distances, but there are time-tested methods of doing so that have worked for thousands of coaches and millions of runners—and that don't involve pain and anguish.

That's where a training plan comes in. Though there are an infinite number of marathon and half-marathon training programs, they all follow certain basic principles that have been proven to help a runner develop the endurance required to run 13.1 or 26.2 miles without getting injured. These programs systematically ramp up mileage and intensity so you gradually push yourself faster and farther than you've gone before. They follow hard efforts with rest days to stave off injury and burnout. There is as much payoff for your mind as there is for your body. Two to 4 months is a long time to train; the practice you get in training will help you develop the mental grit and the emotional toughness to gut it out on race day. You'll be much more confident stepping to the starting line knowing that you have gotten through 20-mile-long runs, speed sessions, and many, many days when you would have preferred to sleep in.

Start Slow and Build Gradually. The body needs time to adapt to training changes and jumps in mileage or intensity. Muscles and joints need recovery time so they can handle more training demands. If you rush that process, you could break down your body rather than building it up. Coaches have found that the best way to avoid injury is to follow the 10 percent rule: Increase your weekly mileage and the length of your long run by no more than 10 percent each week.

Run Easy Most of the Time. About 80 percent of your runs are going to be done at an easy pace that's about 60 to 90 *12 min miles* seconds slower than your goal race pace. The pace should feel comfortable enough for you to hold a conversation while you run. If you're huffing and puffing, you're going too fast.

Alternate Between Hard and Easy Efforts. During the recovery periods that follow hard workouts, your body rebuilds and repairs the muscle tissue that's been damaged and broken down during the harder workouts. Through that rebuilding process, your body gets stronger and more resistant to fatigue at faster paces and longer distances. If you don't push your body far enough or fast enough, you'll never develop the ability to run farther or faster without tiring. If you overload your body

7

too much or you don't rest enough, you'll get injured.

Run Long Every Week. The long run is the cornerstone of marathon and half-marathon training. It helps you build endurance, get used to spending time on your feet, and practice the eating, drinking, gear, and bathroom logistics you'll need to get straightened out for race day. You'll also get emotionally and mentally prepared to spend hours at a time running, just as you'll have to do when you go 13.1 or 26.2.

Hit the Hills. During the first half of your training, you should include one day of running on the hilliest route you can find. Hills build leg and lung power, which will give you the muscle and stamina you need to run faster later in the program. They'll also help prepare you for hills you might face in the race.

Run at Tempo Pace. Tempo runs teach your body to run faster before fatiguing. How? They help you raise your lactate threshold pace, the speed you're able to run at before lactic acid begins accumulating in your leg muscles more rapidly than they can recycle it into usable fuel. When this happens, your muscles begin to perform less efficiently. The higher you push your lactate threshold through appropriate training, the farther and faster you can run before tiring. Tempo pace is typically about 35 seconds faster than your goal marathon pace, or slightly faster than half-marathon pace. Tempo runs should last for 20 to 35 minutes, and your effort level should be "comfortably hard." Treat the tempo run

as a hard workout, and follow it with a day of rest or easy running.

Run at Race Pace. Throughout the *Runner's World* training plans, you'll find lots of runs designated as marathon pace (MP) and half-marathon pace (HMP). It's important to get as much practice as possible running your race pace during training. That way, on the day of your big event, your body will just be able to dial into it, and it will feel like your body's natural rhythm.

Run Fast Once a Week. Even if you're not competitive, running faster once a week is a great way to improve your fitness and your race times. It will also build cardiovascular strength because your heart will be forced to pump harder to deliver oxygen to your leg muscles. Also, your leg muscles will get stronger and more efficient at extracting oxygen from your blood. And as your legs and feet turn over at a quicker rate, you'll shed sloppiness in your stride and run more efficiently.

Taper. During the final weeks leading up to the marathon or half-marathon, drop your weekly mileage by 25 to 50 percent, but keep the intensity of the workouts high. The idea is to let your muscles recover from the buildup of mileage and intensity and adapt to the stresses of training so that you get to race day feeling fresh and ready to run your best.

Measure Your Effort. Training for a marathon or a half-marathon is all about running with purpose. Each workout has a goal—to build endurance, make you faster, or help you recover. It's important to

measure your effort while you're training to make sure that you're working out at the right intensity and you're reaping the benefit. There are a variety of ways to gauge your effort; pace, heart rate, and the talk test have all been proven to be effective.

Cross-Train. Cross-training is a great way to maintain your cardiovascular fitness while giving your body a break from the pounding of running. Activities like yoga, Pilates, and strength training can help build muscle and promote recovery. Swimming, cycling, elliptical training, and rowing will burn a lot of calories and improve your aerobic fitness. They also help you develop a strong upper body, which can help you run faster with less effort and maintain good form in the late stages of a race, when you're fatigued.

Watch Your Form. When you're just starting to run, don't worry too much about your form; your body will naturally gravitate toward its most efficient way of running. That said, there are a few basics to running form that will help you run more comfortably. The basics:

- Look ahead.
- Drop your shoulders.
- Run tall.
- Swing your arms.
- Loosen your grip.
- Plant your feet.
- Maintain a short stride.

Warm Up and Cool Down. Taking the time to ease in and out of a run can make the running feel easier and can help you avoid injury. A 5- to 10-minute warmup will gradually raise your heart and breathing rates, get blood flowing to your muscles, and get them prepared for the work ahead.

Measure Your Effort

TYPE OF RUN	PACE	HEART RATE	TALK TEST
Easy Run	90–150 seconds/mile slower than 5-K pace	65–70% of max heart rate	Complete sentences
Marathon-Pace Run	45–100 seconds/mile slower than 5-K pace	88–92% of max heart rate	Short sentences
Half Marathon– Pace Run	25–50 seconds/mile slower than 5-K pace	92–94% of max heart rate	A few words at a time
Speedwork (800s, 1200s)	5–15 seconds/mile faster than 5-K pace	98–100% of max heart rate	Can't ... talk ... must ... run ...
Tempo Run	20–40 seconds/mile slower than 5-K pace	94–96% of max heart rate	A few words at a time
Yasso 800s*	See below	96–98% of max heart rate	A few words at a time
Long Run	90–150 seconds/mile slower than 5-K pace	65–70% of max heart rate	Complete sentences

*Yasso 800s are done at goal marathon pace in minutes and seconds. So if you're shooting for a 4-hour marathon, you'd aim to run each Yasso 800 in 4 minutes. If you want to finish a marathon in 3 hours and 30 minutes, you'd try to complete each Yasso 800 in 3 minutes and 30 seconds.

PART 2

NUTRITION

People don't start training for a marathon or half-marathon so that they can eat more fruits and vegetables. In fact, most people joke that the sole reason to run long distances is to burn off a double-cheese pizza or earn the right to spend quality time with Ben & Jerry.

But every runner learns it one way or another: When you're prepping for a marathon or half-marathon, you can't run to eat, you gotta eat to run.

When you're in training, food becomes fuel. It will energize your run and help repair muscle tissue after a hard workout so that you can bounce back quickly for your next run.

Try to fuel up on Krispy Kreme or down a five-course meal before you go out and you could hit the wall halfway through or end up spending most of your run crouching in the bushes. Have a big meal the night before a long run and you could wake up with a food hangover: You still feel full and have the aftertaste of last night's meal, yet you're slightly hungry at the same time.

You can do all the training you want, but if you don't eat and drink the right things and get to know your own gut, it doesn't matter if you've got the leg and lung power of an Olympian: Your stomach will take you down every time.

Everyday Eating

Even if you're not looking to lose weight, as you start marathon or half-marathon training, you need the right mix of foods and nutrients to feel good on your runs and to stay injury-free. About 55 percent of your daily calories should come from carbs, 25 percent should come from protein, and another 15 to 20 percent should come from unsaturated fats. But there's no need to start carrying around a calculator. Don't obsess. At each meal, just devote half of your plate to carbs, one-quarter of your plate to protein, and another quarter to healthy fats.

Throughout training, your nutrition needs are going to change. During the first few weeks, when you're building your base and your weekly mileage and intensity remain low, you're not going to need as much fuel as you will later in training, when you're doing speedwork and long runs.

Here is a guide to designing your diet to suit your needs throughout the stages of training.

Eating on the Run

When you're on the road for less than 75 minutes, you can rely on water, sports drinks, and your body's own glycogen stores. Any longer, and you begin to deplete those stores. Your muscles run out of fuel, and your body—not to mention your attitude—starts to drag. Consuming carbs midrun can keep your blood sugar steady so you don't crash and burn.

Weeks 1-6 (marathon) and Weeks 1-4 (half-marathon)

During the first few weeks of training, you're building your base and gradually increasing your mileage. If you want to lose weight, focus on doing it during this phase. You don't want to be slashing calories during the heaviest speed sessions and long runs later.

	TYPE OF ACTIVITY	AMOUNT NEEDED DAILY*
Carbs	Moderate-duration and low-intensity training (30 minutes/day at a conversational pace)	2.5 g/lb of body weight/day
	Moderate to heavy training (1 hour/day)	3-4 g/lb of body weight/day
	Extreme training (>4-6 hours/day)	5 g/lb of body weight/day
Protein		0.7 g/lb of body weight/day
Fats		0.4 g/lb of body weight/day

Weeks 7-13 (marathon) and Weeks 5-8 (half-marathon)

As you start to hit the track for speedwork and your long runs stretch to 15 to 20 miles, you're going to need to rely on all the nutrients to fuel your workouts and aid recovery. If you were trying to shed pounds, it's best not to do it now.

Carbs	3 g/lb of body weight/day
Protein	0.75 g/lb of body weight/day
Fats	0.4 g/lb of body weight/day

Weeks 14-16 (marathon) and Weeks 9-10 (half-marathon)

As you taper for the race, running fewer miles but keeping up the intensity, you're going to need more carbs to restock those glycogen stores so your muscles are primed and ready to run fast.

Carbs	3.5 g/lb of body weight/day; increase to 5 g/lb during race week
Protein	0.7 g/lb of body weight/day
Fats	0.4 g/lb of body weight/day

Race Day and Recovery

Whether you cover 26.2 or 13.1 miles, it's best to take a few weeks to recover by cross-training and running fewer miles. It's common to gain weight during this time. Avoid that by decreasing your consumption of calories and nutrients.

Carbs	2.5 g/lb of body weight/day
Protein	0.6 g/lb of body weight/day
Fats	0.4 g/lb of body weight/day

*Amount needed daily is an average and is based on recent clinical research and findings, as well as anecdotal evidence provided by runners.

Prerun Fueling

TYPE OF RUN	HOW MUCH TO EAT	WHEN TO EAT IT
Up to 75 minutes	100–200 calories of high-carb, low-fat, low-fiber food	30–60 minutes before your run
75 minutes or longer	300 calories for each hour before the run	60–120 minutes before your run
Speed session (mile repeats, tempo runs, Yasso 800s)	High-carb meal or 100- to 200-calorie high-carb snack	2–3 hours before your run for a regular meal; 30 minutes before your run for a snack

Experiment with different brands and flavors of energy gels and sports drinks, and find out what sits well in your stomach. Each brand has its own proprietary blend of sugars and other ingredients. You may respond better to one than another, and you may prefer certain flavors or textures.

Eating on the Run

In order to avoid common pitfalls associated with fueling on the go, follow these rules of the road.

Practice, practice, practice. Train your gut during long runs so that it's accustomed to receiving foods and fluids while on the go.

Watch what you eat. Look at the nutrition content of each gel, chew, or other fuel source you're using. Follow the instructions to determine how much water to consume with each source.

Chase it with water. Always chase gels, chews, or blocks with water. Try to wash them down with a sports drink and you'll end up taking unwanted bathroom stops or feeling nauseated.

Carry it on. Find a lightweight, comfortable waist pack or fuel belt to easily carry your sport beans, gels, or chews. Some running shorts also include pockets designed to carry gels and chews. If you don't have gear, try fastening the packages to your shorts with safety pins.

Pack your own. When your hands are slippery, packages of gels or chews can be tricky to open on the go. Try taking your gels or chews out of their original packages and putting them in a snack-size zipper-lock bag for your long run or race.

Take it slow. Eat your gels, beans, or chews slowly. Trying to gulp down all of the fuel in one quick bite could cause you to choke or to feel sick to your stomach.

Eating for Recovery

What you do in the half hour following a long run or a hard workout can determine the quality of your next run and whether or not you can stay injury-free throughout training, says Suzanne Girard Eberle, MS, RD, CSSD, a board-certified sports dietitian and author of *Endurance Sports Nutrition*.

Refueling. Refueling is important but especially if you're out for an intense effort—such as an interval session, a tempo run, or a long run of 1 hour or more—that taxes your muscles and drains your muscle glycogen stores. For a 30-minute easy run at less than 60 percent of maximum heart rate, refueling isn't going to be as critical. Even so, Eberle recommends eating right away, just to get into the habit of tying your meals to your workouts.

How many carbs do you need for recovery? Divide your weight in half and eat that many grams of carbs. (A 120-pound runner would aim for 60 grams.) Make sure your meal has a carbs-to-protein ratio of 4:1. (Meaning that same 120-pound runner would aim for about 15 grams of protein.) Don't stress about hitting the exact ratio; just make sure you're getting both carbs and protein. Then try to eat that same balance of carbs and protein 2 hours later.

Hydration. Hydration is probably just as important postrun. Fluids regulate body temperature, move waste from your body, ensure that your joints are adequately lubricated, and help flush out the damaged cells that can lead to inflammation. If you're dehydrated, "the body has to work that much harder to perform all those functions," says Eberle. As a result, you're going to feel fatigue, and it's going to take longer to recover. Also, proper hydration can help control cravings, which is important because it's often easy to mistake thirst for hunger.

While there's no set recommendation for daily fluid intake, a good rule of thumb is to aim to drink about half of your body weight in ounces each day. (So if you weigh 150 pounds, drink 75 ounces of water.) And you don't have to just guzzle water. Fruits and vegetables, which are about 80 percent water, can also help you stay hydrated. Plus they're packed with antioxidants, which boost muscle recovery and immunity.

PART 3
INJURY PREVENTION

The most difficult challenge to conquer in any race, we often say, is getting to the starting line. Yet when most people sign up for marathons and half-marathons, they don't realize how formidable that challenge is. We are constantly inundated with e-mails telling us about stress fractures, strained tendons, screaming IT bands, raging cases of plantar fasciitis, torn hamstrings, and runner's knee, not to mention sunburns and bloody blisters. In nearly every case, regardless of which body part is broken or bruised, the emotional fallout is usually worse than the physical injury. Indeed, what runners often find once they get into training is that once you start to reap the emotional, social, and physical benefits of the sport, plus gain daily satisfaction from working toward your goal, it becomes much tougher to rest than to run.

But in order to get to that starting line healthy and safe, you've got to follow a few key principles, which you'll find outlined in the next 2 pages.

Top 10 Ways to Train Injury-Free

1. Build mileage gradually.
2. Listen to your body.
3. Shorten your stride.
4. Strength train to balance your body.
5. At first sign of pain, rest and use ice, compression, and elevation (RICE) for immediate relief.
6. Run on a level surface.
7. Don't race or do speed-work too often.
8. Cross-train for active rest and recovery.
9. Get shoes that fit.
10. Be flexible with your plans.

Tips for Running in the Heat

1. Run a shorter distance than you might normally run in cooler weather.
2. Run slower than you would in cooler weather. Don't expect to match the times that you achieved in better conditions; it's not possible in the heat.
3. Run with friends, or let someone know where you're running and when you'll return.
4. Give yourself 8 to 14 days to acclimate to hot weather, gradually increasing the length and intensity of your training. In that time, your body will learn to decrease your heart rate, decrease your core temperature, and increase your sweat rate.

5. Run at the coolest time of day, usually in the morning before or just after sunrise.
6. Run in the shade—on trails or tree-lined roads—to avoid heat gain from direct sun.
7. Wear light fabrics and as little clothing as possible to encourage the evaporation of sweat.
8. Listen to your body, and back off when something doesn't feel right.
9. Hydrate appropriately before, during, and after your run. But be careful not to overhydrate; that can lead to hyponatremia, a potentially fatal condition resulting from overly diluted blood.

Tips for Running in the Cold

1. Cover your extremities (hands, ears, toes, fingers).
2. Cover your mouth to warm up cold air before it enters your lungs.
3. Dress in thin, light layers that you add or shed.
4. Dress as though it's 20° warmer. Within a few minutes, your core temperature will rise.
5. Watch the wind chill, or how cold it actually feels once the wind hits your skin. If the temperature is 0°F and the wind is blowing at 15 mph, the wind chill is -19°F (-27°C) and you can develop frostbite on exposed skin in 30 minutes or less.
6. Warm up inside by running in place, stairclimbing, or jumping jacks.
7. Eat and drink as you would on regular training days.
8. Change wet clothes for warm ones as soon as you can.
9. Shorten your stride to maintain stable footing on slippery surfaces. Snow is most slippery when it's freezing (32°F).
10. Take it to the treadmill; some days conditions might not be safe or worth the risk of falling.
11. Run midday when temperatures are the warmest and the sun is at its strongest.

Staying Safe on the Road

1. Don't assume a driver sees you. Imagine that a driver can't see you.
2. Always run facing traffic so you can react to any sudden moves of a motorist.
3. At stop signs or lights, wait for drivers to wave you through— then acknowledge with your own wave before crossing.
4. Allow at least 3 feet between you and passing vehicles.
5. Be prepared to jump onto the sidewalk or shoulder of the road.
6. During group runs, go single file when cars need to pass.
7. Use hand signals to show which way you plan to turn.
8. Run with ID or carry a cell phone with emergency contacts.
9. Wear highly visible, brightly colored clothing, and if running in the dark, wear a headlamp or use a flashlight.
10. If you run with headphones, use one earbud so you can hear approaching vehicles.
11. If you run in the dark, watch out for impaired drivers.

HALF-MARATHON PLAN

Beginner

MON	TUES	WED	THURS	FRI	SAT	SUN	TOTAL
Rest/XT	2 miles	Rest/XT	4 miles	Rest/XT	2 miles	5 miles LSD	13 miles

Intermediate

MON	TUES	WED	THURS	FRI	SAT	SUN	TOTAL
Rest/XT	4 miles	Rest/XT	5 miles total, with 3 miles @ HMP	4 miles	Rest/XT	8 miles LSD	21 miles

Advanced

MON	TUES	WED	THURS	FRI	SAT	SUN	TOTAL
Rest/XT	5 miles	5 miles	6 miles total, with 4 miles @ HMP	5 miles	Rest/XT	10 miles LSD	31 miles

Key of running terms appears on last page.

MARATHON PLAN

Beginner

MON	TUES	WED	THURS	FRI	SAT	SUN	TOTAL
Rest	3 miles	Rest	4 miles	Rest	3 miles	5 miles LSD	**15 miles**

Intermediate

MON	TUES	WED	THURS	FRI	SAT	SUN	TOTAL
Rest	4 miles easy	4 miles hills	Rest	5 miles easy	4 miles easy	9 miles LSD	**25 miles**

Advanced

MON	TUES	WED	THUR	FRI	SAT	SUN	TOTAL
4 miles easy	4 miles easy	6 miles hills	4 miles easy	Rest	5 miles easy	10 miles LSD	**33 miles**

Key of running terms appears on last page.

✓ Sunday &
☑ **Monday**
○ **Tuesday**
○ **Wednesday**
○ **Thursday**
○ **Friday**
○ **Saturday**
○ **Sunday**

Rest

>80°-90°

DATE: 7/8/2013   9:04AM
ROUTE: Coopersburg
DISTANCE: 6 miles   Sunday
TIME: 1:05:52 / 10:59 pace
FUEL / HMP
BEFORE: cupcake; allergy med; 2 advil
DURING: ~~H2O~~
AFTER: protein shake
CROSS-TRAINING:
golf Monday

545cal

Rate how you felt before the run (1 being the worst and 10 being the best):

1 2 3 4 5 6 7 ⑧ 9 10

GOALS AND GOAL CHECK-IN:

Lap 1	11:22:04
2	10:57:55
3	10:18:60
4	11:00:74
5	11:34:91
6	10:38.92

Any major obstacles?

Any major accomplishments?

Did you run with anyone? ○ Yes ⊘ No
If yes, who?

Rate how you felt after the run (1 being the worst and 10 being the best):

1 2 3 4 5 6 7 8 9 (10)

OTHER NOTES OR COMMENTS (WEATHER, INJURIES, ETC.):

Started strong and slow. Easier to
get through first 2 miles

Stretched on mat and rolled

No ITB or other issues to report

Had headache - took 2 advil

○ **Monday**
● **Tuesday**
○ **Wednesday**
○ **Thursday**
○ **Friday**
○ **Saturday**
○ **Sunday**

DATE: 6/11
ROUTE: Treadmill
DISTANCE: 2.5 miles
TIME: 1215 PM
FUEL
 BEFORE: yogurt & oatmeal breakfast
 DURING: none
 AFTER: protein shake & 4 pcs ravioli
CROSS-TRAINING:
3 sets of 10 pull ups
3 sets of 10 tricep dips

Rate how you felt before the run (1 being the worst and 10 being the best):

1 2 3 4 5 6 ⑦ 8 9 10

GOALS AND GOAL CHECK-IN:

_____
_____
_____
_____
_____
_____
_____
_____
_____
_____
_____

Any major obstacles?

Any major accomplishments? .5 with an 8.5 incline

Did you run with anyone? ○ Yes ⊗ No
If yes, who?

Rate how you felt after the run (1 being the worst and 10 being the best):

1 2 3 4 5 6 7 (8) 9 10

OTHER NOTES OR COMMENTS (WEATHER, INJURIES, ETC.):

Hard run. Started with 10 min pace
then went to 8:30 min pace, couldn't
push. Music definitely helps.

Tried to walk on incline to compensate
then started running slowly on incline

✱ Note: ITB was definitely aggravated

- ○ **Monday**
- ✗ **Tuesday**
- ○ **Wednesday**
- ○ **Thursday**
- ○ **Friday**
- ○ **Saturday**
- ○ **Sunday**

Rest

DATE: 7/10/2013

ROUTE: Dreadmill

DISTANCE: 2 miles

TIME: 25 mins

FUEL

BEFORE:

DURING:

AFTER:

CROSS-TRAINING: Bike 10 mins
Upper Body

Rate how you felt before the run (1 being the worst and 10 being the best):

1 2 3 4 5 (6) 7 8 9 10

GOALS AND GOAL CHECK-IN:

Felt Stronger
It was warm in the gym.
20 mins at slow pace
Started at 12-11-10-830
then 30 sec 8's and 730s
followed by 60 sec 1145s

Any major obstacles?

Any major accomplishments?

Did you run with anyone? ○ Yes ☒ No
If yes, who?

Rate how you felt after the run (1 being the worst and 10 being the best):

1   2   3   4   5   6   7   8   9   (10)

OTHER NOTES OR COMMENTS (WEATHER, INJURIES, ETC.):

Ham Hamstrings hurt a bit

○ **Monday**
○ **Tuesday**
○ **Wednesday**
⊗ **Thursday**
○ **Friday**
○ **Saturday**
○ **Sunday**

golf

DATE:

ROUTE:

DISTANCE:

TIME:

FUEL

BEFORE:

DURING:

AFTER:

CROSS-TRAINING:

Rate how you felt before the run (1 being the worst and 10 being the best):

1 2 3 4 5 6 7 8 9 10

GOALS AND GOAL CHECK-IN:

_____

_____

_____

_____

_____

_____

_____

_____

_____

_____

_____

Any major obstacles?

Any major accomplishments?

Did you run with anyone? ○ Yes ○ No
If yes, who?

Rate how you felt after the run (1 being the worst and 10 being the best):

1 2 3 4 5 6 7 8 9 10

OTHER NOTES OR COMMENTS (WEATHER, INJURIES, ETC.):

_____

_____

_____

_____

_____

_____

_____

_____

_____

_____

_____

_____

- ○ **Monday**
- ○ **Tuesday**
- ○ **Wednesday**
- ○ **Thursday**
- ○ **Friday**
- ○ **Saturday**
- ○ **Sunday**

DATE:

ROUTE:

DISTANCE:

TIME:

FUEL

  BEFORE:

  DURING:

  AFTER:

CROSS-TRAINING:

Rate how you felt before the run (1 being the worst and 10 being the best):

1   2   3   4   5   6   7   8   9   10

GOALS AND GOAL CHECK-IN:

_____

_____

_____

_____

_____

_____

_____

_____

_____

_____

_____

Any major obstacles?

Any major accomplishments?

Did you run with anyone? ○ Yes ○ No
If yes, who?

Rate how you felt after the run (1 being the worst and 10 being the best):

1 2 3 4 5 6 7 8 9 10

OTHER NOTES OR COMMENTS (WEATHER, INJURIES, ETC.):

_____

_____

_____

_____

_____

_____

_____

_____

_____

_____

_____

_____

○ **Monday**
○ **Tuesday**
○ **Wednesday**
○ **Thursday**
○ **Friday**
○ **Saturday**
○ **Sunday**

DATE:

ROUTE:

DISTANCE:

TIME:

FUEL

  BEFORE:

  DURING:

  AFTER:

CROSS-TRAINING:

Rate how you felt before the run (1 being the worst and 10 being the best):

1 2 3 4 5 6 7 8 9 10

GOALS AND GOAL CHECK-IN:

_____

_____

_____

_____

_____

_____

_____

_____

_____

_____

_____

Any major obstacles?

Any major accomplishments?

Did you run with anyone? ○ Yes ○ No
  If yes, who?

Rate how you felt after the run (1 being the worst and 10 being the best):

1 2 3 4 5 6 7 8 9 10

OTHER NOTES OR COMMENTS (WEATHER, INJURIES, ETC.):

○ **Monday**
○ **Tuesday**
○ **Wednesday**
○ **Thursday**
○ **Friday**
○ **Saturday**
○ **Sunday**

DATE:

ROUTE:

DISTANCE:

TIME:

FUEL

BEFORE:

DURING:

AFTER:

CROSS-TRAINING:

Rate how you felt before the run (1 being the worst and 10 being the best):

1   2   3   4   5   6   7   8   9   10

GOALS AND GOAL CHECK-IN:

_____

_____

_____

_____

_____

_____

_____

_____

_____

_____

_____

Any major obstacles?

Any major accomplishments?

Did you run with anyone? ○ Yes ○ No
If yes, who?

Rate how you felt after the run (1 being the worst and 10 being the best):

1   2   3   4   5   6   7   8   9   10

OTHER NOTES OR COMMENTS (WEATHER, INJURIES, ETC.):

_____
_____
_____
_____
_____
_____
_____
_____
_____
_____
_____
_____

HALF-MARATHON PLAN

Beginner

MON	TUES	WED	THURS	FRI	SAT	SUN	TOTAL
Rest/XT	2 miles	Rest/XT	5 miles	Rest/XT	2 miles	6 miles LSD	**15 miles**

Intermediate

MON	TUES	WED	THURS	FRI	SAT	SUN	TOTAL
Rest/XT	5 miles	Rest/XT	Mile repeats 5 miles with 2 x 1 mile	4 miles	Rest/XT	8 miles LSD	**22 miles**

Advanced

MON	TUES	WED	THURS	FRI	SAT	SUN	TOTAL
Rest/XT	6 miles	5 miles	Mile repeats 7 miles with 3 x 1 mile	5 miles	Rest/XT	10 miles LSD	**33 miles**

Key of running terms appears on last page.

MARATHON PLAN

Beginner

MON	TUES	WED	THURS	FRI	SAT	SUN	TOTAL
Rest	3 miles	Rest	3 miles	Rest	4 miles	7 miles LSD	**17 miles**

Intermediate

MON	TUES	WED	THURS	FRI	SAT	SUN	TOTAL
Rest	4 miles easy	5 miles hills	Rest	5 miles easy	5 miles easy	9 miles LSD	**28 miles**

Advanced

MON	TUES	WED	THURS	FRI	SAT	SUN	TOTAL
5 miles easy	6 miles hills	4 miles easy	6 miles total, with 4 miles @ MP	Rest	5 miles easy	12 miles LSD	**38 miles**

Key of running terms appears on last page.

- ○ **Monday**
- ○ **Tuesday**
- ○ **Wednesday**
- ○ **Thursday**
- ○ **Friday**
- ○ **Saturday**
- ○ **Sunday**

DATE:

ROUTE:

DISTANCE:

TIME:

FUEL

BEFORE:

DURING:

AFTER:

CROSS-TRAINING:

Rate how you felt before the run (1 being the worst and 10 being the best):

1 2 3 4 5 6 7 8 9 10

GOALS AND GOAL CHECK-IN:

_____

_____

_____

_____

_____

_____

_____

_____

_____

_____

_____

Any major obstacles?

Any major accomplishments?

Did you run with anyone? ○ Yes ○ No
If yes, who?

Rate how you felt after the run (1 being the worst and 10 being the best):

1 2 3 4 5 6 7 8 9 10

OTHER NOTES OR COMMENTS (WEATHER, INJURIES, ETC.):

_____

_____

_____

_____

_____

_____

_____

_____

_____

_____

_____

_____

○ **Monday**

○ **Tuesday**

○ **Wednesday**

○ **Thursday**

○ **Friday**

○ **Saturday**

○ **Sunday**

DATE:

ROUTE:

DISTANCE:

TIME:

FUEL

BEFORE:

DURING:

AFTER:

CROSS-TRAINING:

Rate how you felt before the run (1 being the worst and 10 being the best):

1   2   3   4   5   6   7   8   9   10

GOALS AND GOAL CHECK-IN:

_____
_____
_____
_____
_____
_____
_____
_____
_____
_____
_____
_____

Any major obstacles?

Any major accomplishments?

Did you run with anyone? ○ Yes ○ No
If yes, who?

Rate how you felt after the run (1 being the worst and 10 being the best):

1 2 3 4 5 6 7 8 9 10

OTHER NOTES OR COMMENTS (WEATHER, INJURIES, ETC.):

○ **Monday**
○ **Tuesday**
○ **Wednesday**
○ **Thursday**
○ **Friday**
○ **Saturday**
○ **Sunday**

DATE:

ROUTE:

DISTANCE:

TIME:

FUEL

  BEFORE:

  DURING:

  AFTER:

CROSS-TRAINING:

Rate how you felt before the run (1 being the worst and 10 being the best):

1　2　3　4　5　6　7　8　9　10

GOALS AND GOAL CHECK-IN:

_____

_____

_____

_____

_____

_____

_____

_____

_____

_____

_____

Any major obstacles?

Any major accomplishments?

Did you run with anyone? ○ Yes ○ No
If yes, who?

Rate how you felt after the run (1 being the worst and 10 being the best):

1 2 3 4 5 6 7 8 9 10

OTHER NOTES OR COMMENTS (WEATHER, INJURIES, ETC.):

_____

_____

_____

_____

_____

_____

_____

_____

_____

_____

_____

_____

○ **Monday**

○ **Tuesday**

○ **Wednesday**

○ **Thursday**

○ **Friday**

○ **Saturday**

○ **Sunday**

DATE:

ROUTE:

DISTANCE:

TIME:

FUEL

  BEFORE:

  DURING:

  AFTER:

CROSS-TRAINING:

Rate how you felt before the run (1 being the worst and 10 being the best):

1 2 3 4 5 6 7 8 9 10

GOALS AND GOAL CHECK-IN:

_____

_____

_____

_____

_____

_____

_____

_____

_____

_____

_____

Any major obstacles?

Any major accomplishments?

Did you run with anyone? ○ Yes ○ No
If yes, who?

Rate how you felt after the run (1 being the worst and 10 being the best):

1 2 3 4 5 6 7 8 9 10

OTHER NOTES OR COMMENTS (WEATHER, INJURIES, ETC.):

_____

_____

_____

_____

_____

_____

_____

_____

_____

_____

_____

_____

_____

○ **Monday**
○ **Tuesday**
○ **Wednesday**
○ **Thursday**
○ **Friday**
○ **Saturday**
○ **Sunday**

DATE:

ROUTE:

DISTANCE:

TIME:

FUEL

BEFORE:

DURING:

AFTER:

CROSS-TRAINING:

Rate how you felt before the run (1 being the worst and 10 being the best):

1 2 3 4 5 6 7 8 9 10

GOALS AND GOAL CHECK-IN:

Any major obstacles?

Any major accomplishments?

Did you run with anyone? ○ Yes ○ No

If yes, who?

Rate how you felt after the run (1 being the worst and 10 being the best):

1   2   3   4   5   6   7   8   9   10

OTHER NOTES OR COMMENTS (WEATHER, INJURIES, ETC.):

_____

_____

_____

_____

_____

_____

_____

_____

_____

_____

_____

_____

- ○ **Monday**
- ○ **Tuesday**
- ○ **Wednesday**
- ○ **Thursday**
- ○ **Friday**
- ○ **Saturday**
- ○ **Sunday**

DATE:

ROUTE:

DISTANCE:

TIME:

FUEL

BEFORE:

DURING:

AFTER:

CROSS-TRAINING:

Rate how you felt before the run (1 being the worst and 10 being the best):

1   2   3   4   5   6   7   8   9   10

GOALS AND GOAL CHECK-IN:

_____

_____

_____

_____

_____

_____

_____

_____

_____

_____

_____

Any major obstacles?

Any major accomplishments?

Did you run with anyone? ○ Yes ○ No
If yes, who?

Rate how you felt after the run (1 being the worst and 10 being the best):

1 2 3 4 5 6 7 8 9 10

OTHER NOTES OR COMMENTS (WEATHER, INJURIES, ETC.):

○ **Monday**
○ **Tuesday**
○ **Wednesday**
○ **Thursday**
○ **Friday**
○ **Saturday**
○ **Sunday**

DATE:

ROUTE:

DISTANCE:

TIME:

FUEL

BEFORE:

DURING:

AFTER:

CROSS-TRAINING:

Rate how you felt before the run (1 being the worst and 10 being the best):

1 2 3 4 5 6 7 8 9 10

GOALS AND GOAL CHECK-IN:

Any major obstacles?

Any major accomplishments?

Did you run with anyone? ○ Yes ○ No
   If yes, who?

Rate how you felt after the run (1 being the worst and 10 being the best):

1 2 3 4 5 6 7 8 9 10

OTHER NOTES OR COMMENTS (WEATHER, INJURIES, ETC.):

_____

_____

_____

_____

_____

_____

_____

_____

_____

_____

_____

_____

HALF-MARATHON PLAN

Beginner

MON	TUES	WED	THURS	FRI	SAT	SUN	TOTAL
Rest/XT	2 miles	Rest/XT	5 miles total, with 3 miles @ HMP	Rest/XT	2 miles	7 miles LSD	**16 miles**

Intermediate

MON	TUES	WED	THURS	FRI	SAT	SUN	TOTAL
Rest/XT	5 miles	Rest/XT	5 miles total, with 3 miles @ HMP	4 miles	Rest/XT	9 miles LSD	**23 miles**

Advanced

MON	TUES	WED	THURS	FRI	SAT	SUN	TOTAL
Rest/XT	6 miles	6 miles	6 miles total, with 4 miles @ HMP	6 miles	Rest/XT	11 miles LSD	**35 miles**

Key of running terms appears on last page.

MARATHON PLAN

Beginner

MON	TUES	WED	THURS	FRI	SAT	SUN	TOTAL
Rest	3 miles	Rest	4 miles	Rest	4 miles	9 miles LSD	**20 miles**

Intermediate

MON	TUES	WED	THURS	FRI	SAT	SUN	TOTAL
Rest	3 miles easy	5 miles hills	Rest	5 miles easy	5 miles easy	12 miles LSD	**30 miles**

Advanced

MON	TUES	WED	THURS	FRI	SAT	SUN	TOTAL
4 miles easy	6 miles hills	4 miles easy	8 miles total, with 6 miles @ MP	Rest	5 miles easy	14 miles LSD	**41 miles**

Key of running terms appears on last page.

○ **Monday**
○ **Tuesday**
○ **Wednesday**
○ **Thursday**
○ **Friday**
○ **Saturday**
○ **Sunday**

DATE:

ROUTE:

DISTANCE:

TIME:

FUEL

BEFORE:

DURING:

AFTER:

CROSS-TRAINING:

Rate how you felt before the run (1 being the worst and 10 being the best):

1 2 3 4 5 6 7 8 9 10

GOALS AND GOAL CHECK-IN:

_____

_____

_____

_____

_____

_____

_____

_____

_____

_____

_____

Any major obstacles?

Any major accomplishments?

Did you run with anyone? ○ Yes ○ No
If yes, who?

Rate how you felt after the run (1 being the worst and 10 being the best):

1 2 3 4 5 6 7 8 9 10

OTHER NOTES OR COMMENTS (WEATHER, INJURIES, ETC.):

_____

○ **Monday**
○ **Tuesday**
○ **Wednesday**
○ **Thursday**
○ **Friday**
○ **Saturday**
○ **Sunday**

DATE:

ROUTE:

DISTANCE:

TIME:

FUEL

BEFORE:

DURING:

AFTER:

CROSS-TRAINING:

Rate how you felt before the run (1 being the worst and 10 being the best):

1   2   3   4   5   6   7   8   9   10

GOALS AND GOAL CHECK-IN:

_____

_____

_____

_____

_____

_____

_____

_____

_____

_____

_____

_____

Any major obstacles?

Any major accomplishments?

Did you run with anyone? ○ Yes ○ No

If yes, who?

Rate how you felt after the run (1 being the worst and 10 being the best):

1 2 3 4 5 6 7 8 9 10

OTHER NOTES OR COMMENTS (WEATHER, INJURIES, ETC.):

_____

_____

_____

_____

_____

_____

_____

_____

_____

_____

WEEK 3 DAY 3

○ **Monday**
○ **Tuesday**
○ **Wednesday**
○ **Thursday**
○ **Friday**
○ **Saturday**
○ **Sunday**

DATE:

ROUTE:

DISTANCE:

TIME:

FUEL

BEFORE:

DURING:

AFTER:

CROSS-TRAINING:

Rate how you felt before the run (1 being the worst and 10 being the best):

1   2   3   4   5   6   7   8   9   10

GOALS AND GOAL CHECK-IN:

_____
_____
_____
_____
_____
_____
_____
_____
_____
_____
_____
_____

Any major obstacles?

Any major accomplishments?

Did you run with anyone? ○ Yes ○ No
If yes, who?

Rate how you felt after the run (1 being the worst and 10 being the best):

1 2 3 4 5 6 7 8 9 10

OTHER NOTES OR COMMENTS (WEATHER, INJURIES, ETC.):

_____

_____

_____

_____

_____

_____

_____

_____

_____

_____

- ○ **Monday**
- ○ **Tuesday**
- ○ **Wednesday**
- ○ **Thursday**
- ○ **Friday**
- ○ **Saturday**
- ○ **Sunday**

DATE:

ROUTE:

DISTANCE:

TIME:

FUEL

BEFORE:

DURING:

AFTER:

CROSS-TRAINING:

Rate how you felt before the run (1 being the worst and 10 being the best):

1 2 3 4 5 6 7 8 9 10

GOALS AND GOAL CHECK-IN:

_____

_____

_____

_____

_____

_____

_____

_____

_____

_____

Any major obstacles?

Any major accomplishments?

Did you run with anyone? ○ Yes ○ No
If yes, who?

Rate how you felt after the run (1 being the worst and 10 being the best):

1 2 3 4 5 6 7 8 9 10

OTHER NOTES OR COMMENTS (WEATHER, INJURIES, ETC.):

_____

_____

_____

_____

_____

_____

_____

_____

_____

_____

_____

○ **Monday**
○ **Tuesday**
○ **Wednesday**
○ **Thursday**
○ **Friday**
○ **Saturday**
○ **Sunday**

DATE:

ROUTE:

DISTANCE:

TIME:

FUEL

BEFORE:

DURING:

AFTER:

CROSS-TRAINING:

Rate how you felt before the run (1 being the worst and 10 being the best):

1   2   3   4   5   6   7   8   9   10

GOALS AND GOAL CHECK-IN:

Any major obstacles?

Any major accomplishments?

Did you run with anyone? ○ Yes ○ No
If yes, who?

Rate how you felt after the run (1 being the worst and 10 being the best):

1 2 3 4 5 6 7 8 9 10

OTHER NOTES OR COMMENTS (WEATHER, INJURIES, ETC.):

○ **Monday**

○ **Tuesday**

○ **Wednesday**

○ **Thursday**

○ **Friday**

○ **Saturday**

○ **Sunday**

DATE:

ROUTE:

DISTANCE:

TIME:

FUEL

 BEFORE:

 DURING:

 AFTER:

CROSS-TRAINING:

Rate how you felt before the run (1 being the worst and 10 being the best):

1 2 3 4 5 6 7 8 9 10

GOALS AND GOAL CHECK-IN:

_____

_____

_____

_____

_____

_____

_____

_____

_____

_____

_____

_____

Any major obstacles?

Any major accomplishments?

Did you run with anyone? ○ Yes ○ No
If yes, who?

Rate how you felt after the run (1 being the worst and 10 being the best):

1 2 3 4 5 6 7 8 9 10

OTHER NOTES OR COMMENTS (WEATHER, INJURIES, ETC.):

○ **Monday**
○ **Tuesday**
○ **Wednesday**
○ **Thursday**
○ **Friday**
○ **Saturday**
○ **Sunday**

DATE:

ROUTE:

DISTANCE:

TIME:

FUEL

BEFORE:

DURING:

AFTER:

CROSS-TRAINING:

Rate how you felt before the run (1 being the worst and 10 being the best):

1　2　3　4　5　6　7　8　9　10

GOALS AND GOAL CHECK-IN:

Any major obstacles?

Any major accomplishments?

Did you run with anyone? ○ Yes ○ No
If yes, who?

Rate how you felt after the run (1 being the worst and 10 being the best):

1 2 3 4 5 6 7 8 9 10

OTHER NOTES OR COMMENTS (WEATHER, INJURIES, ETC.):

_____

_____

_____

_____

_____

_____

_____

_____

_____

_____

_____

_____

HALF-MARATHON PLAN

Beginner

MON	TUES	WED	THURS	FRI	SAT	SUN	TOTAL
Rest/XT	2 miles	Rest/XT	6 miles total, with 4 miles @ HMP	Rest/XT	2 miles	7 miles LSD	**17 miles**

Intermediate

MON	TUES	WED	THURS	FRI	SAT	SUN	TOTAL
Rest/XT	5 miles	Rest/XT	6 miles total, with 4 miles @ HMP	4 miles	Rest/XT	9 miles LSD or 10-K race	**24 miles**

Advanced

MON	TUES	WED	THURS	FRI	SAT	SUN	TOTAL
Rest/XT	7 miles	6 miles	7 miles total, with 5 miles @ HMP	6 miles	Rest/XT	11 miles LSD	**37 miles**

Key of running terms appears on last page.

MARATHON PLAN

Beginner

MON	TUES	WED	THURS	FRI	SAT	SUN	TOTAL
Rest	4 miles	Time trial (1 mile)	3 miles	Rest	4 miles	7 miles	**19 miles**

Intermediate

MON	TUES	WED	THURS	FRI	SAT	SUN	TOTAL
Rest	4 miles easy	5 miles hills	Time trial (1 mile)	Rest	4 miles easy	13 miles LSD	**28 miles**

Advanced

MON	TUES	WED	THURS	FRI	SAT	SUN	TOTAL
4 miles easy	5 miles hills	5 miles easy	4 miles total, with 2 miles @ MP	Rest	5 miles easy	10 miles LSD	**33 miles**

Key of running terms appears on last page.

○ **Monday**
○ **Tuesday**
○ **Wednesday**
○ **Thursday**
○ **Friday**
○ **Saturday**
○ **Sunday**

DATE:

ROUTE:

DISTANCE:

TIME:

FUEL
  BEFORE:
  DURING:
  AFTER:

CROSS-TRAINING:

Rate how you felt before the run (1 being the worst and 10 being the best):

1 2 3 4 5 6 7 8 9 10

GOALS AND GOAL CHECK-IN:

_____
_____
_____
_____
_____
_____
_____
_____
_____
_____
_____
_____

Any major obstacles?

Any major accomplishments?

Did you run with anyone?   ○ Yes ○ No

If yes, who?

Rate how you felt after the run (1 being the worst and 10 being the best):

1 2 3 4 5 6 7 8 9 10

OTHER NOTES OR COMMENTS (WEATHER, INJURIES, ETC.):

○ **Monday**
○ **Tuesday**
○ **Wednesday**
○ **Thursday**
○ **Friday**
○ **Saturday**
○ **Sunday**

DATE:

ROUTE:

DISTANCE:

TIME:

FUEL

BEFORE:

DURING:

AFTER:

CROSS-TRAINING:

Rate how you felt before the run (1 being the worst and 10 being the best):

1　2　3　4　5　6　7　8　9　10

GOALS AND GOAL CHECK-IN:

_____

_____

_____

_____

_____

_____

_____

_____

_____

_____

_____

Any major obstacles?

Any major accomplishments?

Did you run with anyone? ○ Yes ○ No
If yes, who?

Rate how you felt after the run (1 being the worst and 10 being the best):

1 2 3 4 5 6 7 8 9 10

OTHER NOTES OR COMMENTS (WEATHER, INJURIES, ETC.):

_____

_____

_____

_____

_____

_____

_____

_____

_____

_____

_____

_____

- ○ **Monday**
- ○ **Tuesday**
- ○ **Wednesday**
- ○ **Thursday**
- ○ **Friday**
- ○ **Saturday**
- ○ **Sunday**

DATE:

ROUTE:

DISTANCE:

TIME:

FUEL

BEFORE:

DURING:

AFTER:

CROSS-TRAINING:

Rate how you felt before the run (1 being the worst and 10 being the best):

1 2 3 4 5 6 7 8 9 10

GOALS AND GOAL CHECK-IN:

_____
_____
_____
_____
_____
_____
_____
_____
_____
_____
_____

Any major obstacles?

Any major accomplishments?

Did you run with anyone? ○ Yes ○ No
If yes, who?

Rate how you felt after the run (1 being the worst and 10 being the best):

1 2 3 4 5 6 7 8 9 10

OTHER NOTES OR COMMENTS (WEATHER, INJURIES, ETC.):

_____
_____
_____
_____
_____
_____
_____
_____
_____
_____
_____
_____
_____

○ **Monday**
○ **Tuesday**
○ **Wednesday**
○ **Thursday**
○ **Friday**
○ **Saturday**
○ **Sunday**

DATE:

ROUTE:

DISTANCE:

TIME:

FUEL

 BEFORE:

 DURING:

 AFTER:

CROSS-TRAINING:

Rate how you felt before the run (1 being the worst and 10 being the best):

1   2   3   4   5   6   7   8   9   10

GOALS AND GOAL CHECK-IN:

_____
_____
_____
_____
_____
_____
_____
_____
_____
_____
_____
_____

Any major obstacles?

Any major accomplishments?

Did you run with anyone? ○ Yes ○ No
If yes, who?

Rate how you felt after the run (1 being the worst and 10 being the best):

1 2 3 4 5 6 7 8 9 10

OTHER NOTES OR COMMENTS (WEATHER, INJURIES, ETC.):

_____
_____
_____
_____
_____
_____
_____
_____
_____
_____
_____

- ○ **Monday**
- ○ **Tuesday**
- ○ **Wednesday**
- ○ **Thursday**
- ○ **Friday**
- ○ **Saturday**
- ○ **Sunday**

DATE:

ROUTE:

DISTANCE:

TIME:

FUEL

BEFORE:

DURING:

AFTER:

CROSS-TRAINING:

Rate how you felt before the run (1 being the worst and 10 being the best):

1 2 3 4 5 6 7 8 9 10

GOALS AND GOAL CHECK-IN:

_____

_____

_____

_____

_____

_____

_____

_____

_____

_____

Any major obstacles?

Any major accomplishments?

Did you run with anyone? ○ Yes ○ No
If yes, who?

Rate how you felt after the run (1 being the worst and 10 being the best):

1 2 3 4 5 6 7 8 9 10

OTHER NOTES OR COMMENTS (WEATHER, INJURIES, ETC.):

○ **Monday**
○ **Tuesday**
○ **Wednesday**
○ **Thursday**
○ **Friday**
○ **Saturday**
○ **Sunday**

DATE:

ROUTE:

DISTANCE:

TIME:

FUEL

  BEFORE:

  DURING:

  AFTER:

CROSS-TRAINING:

Rate how you felt before the run (1 being the worst and 10 being the best):

1   2   3   4   5   6   7   8   9   10

GOALS AND GOAL CHECK-IN:

_____

_____

_____

_____

_____

_____

_____

_____

_____

_____

_____

_____

Any major obstacles?

Any major accomplishments?

Did you run with anyone? ○ Yes ○ No
If yes, who?

Rate how you felt after the run (1 being the worst and 10 being the best):

1 2 3 4 5 6 7 8 9 10

OTHER NOTES OR COMMENTS (WEATHER, INJURIES, ETC.):

_____

_____

_____

_____

_____

_____

_____

_____

_____

_____

WEEK 4 DAY 7

○ **Monday**
○ **Tuesday**
○ **Wednesday**
○ **Thursday**
○ **Friday**
○ **Saturday**
○ **Sunday**

DATE:

ROUTE:

DISTANCE:

TIME:

FUEL

BEFORE:

DURING:

AFTER:

CROSS-TRAINING:

Rate how you felt before the run (1 being the worst and 10 being the best):

1 2 3 4 5 6 7 8 9 10

GOALS AND GOAL CHECK-IN:

_____
_____
_____
_____
_____
_____
_____
_____
_____
_____
_____

Any major obstacles?

Any major accomplishments?

Did you run with anyone? ○ Yes ○ No

If yes, who?

Rate how you felt after the run (1 being the worst and 10 being the best):

1 2 3 4 5 6 7 8 9 10

OTHER NOTES OR COMMENTS (WEATHER, INJURIES, ETC.):

_____

_____

_____

_____

_____

_____

_____

_____

_____

_____

_____

HALF-MARATHON PLAN

Beginner

MON	TUES	WED	THURS	FRI	SAT	SUN	TOTAL
Rest/XT	4 miles	Rest/XT	3 miles	Rest/XT	3 miles	4 miles LSD	14 miles

Intermediate

MON	TUES	WED	THURS	FRI	SAT	SUN	TOTAL
Rest/XT	5 miles	3 miles	4 miles	4 miles	Rest/XT	5 miles LSD	21 miles

Advanced

MON	TUES	WED	THURS	FRI	SAT	SUN	TOTAL
Rest/XT	6 miles	6 miles	6 miles	5 miles	Rest/XT	6 miles LSD	29 miles

Key of running terms appears on last page.

MARATHON PLAN

Beginner

MON	TUES	WED	THURS	FRI	SAT	SUN	TOTAL
Rest	4 miles	Rest	3 miles	Rest	5 miles	10 miles LSD	**22 miles**

Intermediate

MON	TUES	WED	THURS	FRI	SAT	SUN	TOTAL
Rest	4 miles easy with 4 strides	7 miles hills	Rest	4 miles total, with 2 miles @ MP	4 miles easy	13 miles LSD	**32 miles**

Advanced

MON	TUES	WED	THURS	FRI	SAT	SUN	TOTAL
3 miles easy with 3 strides	8 miles hills	5 miles easy	8 miles total, with 6 miles @ MP	Rest	4 miles easy	14 miles LSD	**42 miles**

Key of running terms appears on last page.

○ **Monday**

○ **Tuesday**

○ **Wednesday**

○ **Thursday**

○ **Friday**

○ **Saturday**

○ **Sunday**

DATE:

ROUTE:

DISTANCE:

TIME:

FUEL

BEFORE:

DURING:

AFTER:

CROSS-TRAINING:

Rate how you felt before the run (1 being the worst and 10 being the best):

1 2 3 4 5 6 7 8 9 10

GOALS AND GOAL CHECK-IN:

_____

_____

_____

_____

_____

_____

_____

_____

_____

_____

_____

Any major obstacles?

Any major accomplishments?

Did you run with anyone? ○ Yes ○ No

If yes, who?

Rate how you felt after the run (1 being the worst and 10 being the best):

1 2 3 4 5 6 7 8 9 10

OTHER NOTES OR COMMENTS (WEATHER, INJURIES, ETC.):

○ **Monday**
○ **Tuesday**
○ **Wednesday**
○ **Thursday**
○ **Friday**
○ **Saturday**
○ **Sunday**

DATE:

ROUTE:

DISTANCE:

TIME:

FUEL

BEFORE:

DURING:

AFTER:

CROSS-TRAINING:

Rate how you felt before the run (1 being the worst and 10 being the best):

1 2 3 4 5 6 7 8 9 10

GOALS AND GOAL CHECK-IN:

Any major obstacles?

Any major accomplishments?

Did you run with anyone? ○ Yes ○ No
If yes, who?

Rate how you felt after the run (1 being the worst and 10 being the best):

1 2 3 4 5 6 7 8 9 10

OTHER NOTES OR COMMENTS (WEATHER, INJURIES, ETC.):

_____

_____

_____

_____

_____

_____

_____

_____

_____

_____

_____

_____

○ **Monday**

○ **Tuesday**

○ **Wednesday**

○ **Thursday**

○ **Friday**

○ **Saturday**

○ **Sunday**

DATE:

ROUTE:

DISTANCE:

TIME:

FUEL

  BEFORE:

  DURING:

  AFTER:

CROSS-TRAINING:

Rate how you felt before the run (1 being the worst and 10 being the best):

1   2   3   4   5   6   7   8   9   10

GOALS AND GOAL CHECK-IN:

_____

_____

_____

_____

_____

_____

_____

_____

_____

_____

_____

Any major obstacles?

Any major accomplishments?

Did you run with anyone? ○ Yes ○ No
If yes, who?

Rate how you felt after the run (1 being the worst and 10 being the best):

1   2   3   4   5   6   7   8   9   10

OTHER NOTES OR COMMENTS (WEATHER, INJURIES, ETC.):

_____

_____

_____

_____

_____

_____

_____

_____

_____

_____

_____

_____

- ○ **Monday**
- ○ **Tuesday**
- ○ **Wednesday**
- ○ **Thursday**
- ○ **Friday**
- ○ **Saturday**
- ○ **Sunday**

DATE:

ROUTE:

DISTANCE:

TIME:

FUEL

  BEFORE:

  DURING:

  AFTER:

CROSS-TRAINING:

Rate how you felt before the run (1 being the worst and 10 being the best):

1 2 3 4 5 6 7 8 9 10

GOALS AND GOAL CHECK-IN:

_____

_____

_____

_____

_____

_____

_____

_____

_____

_____

_____

Any major obstacles?

Any major accomplishments?

Did you run with anyone?   ○ Yes ○ No

If yes, who?

Rate how you felt after the run (1 being the worst and 10 being the best):

1 2 3 4 5 6 7 8 9 10

OTHER NOTES OR COMMENTS (WEATHER, INJURIES, ETC.):

○ **Monday**

○ **Tuesday**

○ **Wednesday**

○ **Thursday**

○ **Friday**

○ **Saturday**

○ **Sunday**

DATE:

ROUTE:

DISTANCE:

TIME:

FUEL

  BEFORE:

  DURING:

  AFTER:

CROSS-TRAINING:

Rate how you felt before the run (1 being the worst and 10 being the best):

1   2   3   4   5   6   7   8   9   10

GOALS AND GOAL CHECK-IN:

_____

_____

_____

_____

_____

_____

_____

_____

_____

_____

_____

Any major obstacles?

Any major accomplishments?

Did you run with anyone? ○ Yes ○ No
If yes, who?

Rate how you felt after the run (1 being the worst and 10 being the best):

1 2 3 4 5 6 7 8 9 10

OTHER NOTES OR COMMENTS (WEATHER, INJURIES, ETC.):

○ **Monday**
○ **Tuesday**
○ **Wednesday**
○ **Thursday**
○ **Friday**
○ **Saturday**
○ **Sunday**

DATE:

ROUTE:

DISTANCE:

TIME:

FUEL
  BEFORE:
  DURING:
  AFTER:

CROSS-TRAINING:

Rate how you felt before the run (1 being the worst and 10 being the best):

1 2 3 4 5 6 7 8 9 10

GOALS AND GOAL CHECK-IN:

Any major obstacles?

Any major accomplishments?

Did you run with anyone?   ○ Yes ○ No
If yes, who?

Rate how you felt after the run (1 being the worst and 10 being the best):

1   2   3   4   5   6   7   8   9   10

OTHER NOTES OR COMMENTS (WEATHER, INJURIES, ETC.):

_____

_____

_____

_____

_____

_____

_____

_____

_____

_____

_____

○ **Monday**
○ **Tuesday**
○ **Wednesday**
○ **Thursday**
○ **Friday**
○ **Saturday**
○ **Sunday**

DATE:

ROUTE:

DISTANCE:

TIME:

FUEL

  BEFORE:

  DURING:

  AFTER:

CROSS-TRAINING:

Rate how you felt before the run (1 being the worst and 10 being the best):

1 2 3 4 5 6 7 8 9 10

GOALS AND GOAL CHECK-IN:

_____

_____

_____

_____

_____

_____

_____

_____

_____

_____

Any major obstacles?

Any major accomplishments?

Did you run with anyone? ○ Yes ○ No

If yes, who?

Rate how you felt after the run (1 being the worst and 10 being the best):

1 2 3 4 5 6 7 8 9 10

OTHER NOTES OR COMMENTS (WEATHER, INJURIES, ETC.):

_____

_____

_____

_____

_____

_____

_____

_____

_____

_____

_____

_____

HALF-MARATHON PLAN

Beginner

MON	TUES	WED	THURS	FRI	SAT	SUN	TOTAL
Rest/XT	2 miles	Rest/XT	7 miles total, with 3 miles @ HMP	Rest/XT	3 miles	8 miles LSD	**20 miles**

Intermediate

MON	TUES	WED	THURS	FRI	SAT	SUN	TOTAL
Rest/XT	4 miles	Rest/XT	Mile repeats 7 miles with 3 x 1 mile	4 miles	Rest/XT	10 miles LSD	**25 miles**

Advanced

MON	TUES	WED	THURS	FRI	SAT	SUN	TOTAL
Rest/XT	7 miles	6 miles	Mile repeats 8 miles with 4 x 1 mile	6 miles	Rest/XT	12 miles LSD	**39 miles**

Key of running terms appears on last page.

MARATHON PLAN

Beginner

MON	TUES	WED	THURS	FRI	SAT	SUN	TOTAL
Rest	4 miles	Rest	3 miles	Rest	5 miles	12 miles LSD	**24 miles**

Intermediate

MON	TUES	WED	THURS	FRI	SAT	SUN	TOTAL
Rest	5 miles easy with 5 strides	6 miles hills	4 miles total, with 2 miles @ MP	6 miles easy	5 miles easy	15 miles LSD	**36 miles**

Advanced

MON	TUES	WED	THURS	FRI	SAT	SUN	TOTAL
6 miles easy with 6 strides	7 miles hills	5 miles easy	8 miles total, with 6 miles @ MP	Rest	4 miles easy	16 miles LSD	**46 miles**

Key of running terms appears on last page.

○ **Monday**
○ **Tuesday**
○ **Wednesday**
○ **Thursday**
○ **Friday**
○ **Saturday**
○ **Sunday**

DATE:

ROUTE:

DISTANCE:

TIME:

FUEL

BEFORE:

DURING:

AFTER:

CROSS-TRAINING:

Rate how you felt before the run (1 being the worst and 10 being the best):

1 2 3 4 5 6 7 8 9 10

GOALS AND GOAL CHECK-IN:

_____
_____
_____
_____
_____
_____
_____
_____
_____
_____
_____

Any major obstacles?

Any major accomplishments?

Did you run with anyone?   ○ Yes ○ No

If yes, who?

Rate how you felt after the run (1 being the worst and 10 being the best):

1 2 3 4 5 6 7 8 9 10

OTHER NOTES OR COMMENTS (WEATHER, INJURIES, ETC.):

○ **Monday**
○ **Tuesday**
○ **Wednesday**
○ **Thursday**
○ **Friday**
○ **Saturday**
○ **Sunday**

DATE:

ROUTE:

DISTANCE:

TIME:

FUEL

BEFORE:

DURING:

AFTER:

CROSS-TRAINING:

Rate how you felt before the run (1 being the worst and 10 being the best):

1 2 3 4 5 6 7 8 9 10

GOALS AND GOAL CHECK-IN:

_____
_____
_____
_____
_____
_____
_____
_____
_____
_____
_____

Any major obstacles?

Any major accomplishments?

Did you run with anyone? ○ Yes ○ No
If yes, who?

Rate how you felt after the run (1 being the worst and 10 being the best):

1 2 3 4 5 6 7 8 9 10

OTHER NOTES OR COMMENTS (WEATHER, INJURIES, ETC.):

_____

_____

_____

_____

_____

_____

_____

_____

_____

_____

_____

_____

○ **Monday**
○ **Tuesday**
○ **Wednesday**
○ **Thursday**
○ **Friday**
○ **Saturday**
○ **Sunday**

DATE:

ROUTE:

DISTANCE:

TIME:

FUEL

BEFORE:

DURING:

AFTER:

CROSS-TRAINING:

Rate how you felt before the run (1 being the worst and 10 being the best):

1   2   3   4   5   6   7   8   9   10

GOALS AND GOAL CHECK-IN:

_____

_____

_____

_____

_____

_____

_____

_____

_____

_____

_____

Any major obstacles?

Any major accomplishments?

Did you run with anyone? ○ Yes ○ No
If yes, who?

Rate how you felt after the run (1 being the worst and 10 being the best):

1   2   3   4   5   6   7   8   9   10

OTHER NOTES OR COMMENTS (WEATHER, INJURIES, ETC.):

○ **Monday**
○ **Tuesday**
○ **Wednesday**
○ **Thursday**
○ **Friday**
○ **Saturday**
○ **Sunday**

DATE:

ROUTE:

DISTANCE:

TIME:

FUEL

BEFORE:

DURING:

AFTER:

CROSS-TRAINING:

Rate how you felt before the run (1 being the worst and 10 being the best):

1 2 3 4 5 6 7 8 9 10

GOALS AND GOAL CHECK-IN:

_____
_____
_____
_____
_____
_____
_____
_____
_____
_____
_____

Any major obstacles?

Any major accomplishments?

Did you run with anyone? ○ Yes ○ No
If yes, who?

Rate how you felt after the run (1 being the worst and 10 being the best):

1 2 3 4 5 6 7 8 9 10

OTHER NOTES OR COMMENTS (WEATHER, INJURIES, ETC.):

_____

_____

_____

_____

_____

_____

_____

_____

_____

_____

_____

○ **Monday**
○ **Tuesday**
○ **Wednesday**
○ **Thursday**
○ **Friday**
○ **Saturday**
○ **Sunday**

DATE:

ROUTE:

DISTANCE:

TIME:

FUEL

BEFORE:

DURING:

AFTER:

CROSS-TRAINING:

Rate how you felt before the run (1 being the worst and 10 being the best):

1 2 3 4 5 6 7 8 9 10

GOALS AND GOAL CHECK-IN:

_____
_____
_____
_____
_____
_____
_____
_____
_____
_____
_____
_____

Any major obstacles?

Any major accomplishments?

Did you run with anyone? ○ Yes ○ No
If yes, who?

Rate how you felt after the run (1 being the worst and 10 being the best):

1 2 3 4 5 6 7 8 9 10

OTHER NOTES OR COMMENTS (WEATHER, INJURIES, ETC.):

_____

_____

_____

_____

_____

_____

_____

_____

_____

_____

_____

_____

- ○ **Monday**
- ○ **Tuesday**
- ○ **Wednesday**
- ○ **Thursday**
- ○ **Friday**
- ○ **Saturday**
- ○ **Sunday**

DATE:

ROUTE:

DISTANCE:

TIME:

FUEL

 BEFORE:

 DURING:

 AFTER:

CROSS-TRAINING:

Rate how you felt before the run (1 being the worst and 10 being the best):

1 2 3 4 5 6 7 8 9 10

GOALS AND GOAL CHECK-IN:

Any major obstacles?

Any major accomplishments?

Did you run with anyone? ○ Yes ○ No

If yes, who?

Rate how you felt after the run (1 being the worst and 10 being the best):

1 2 3 4 5 6 7 8 9 10

OTHER NOTES OR COMMENTS (WEATHER, INJURIES, ETC.):

_____

_____

_____

_____

_____

_____

_____

_____

_____

_____

_____

○ **Monday**
○ **Tuesday**
○ **Wednesday**
○ **Thursday**
○ **Friday**
○ **Saturday**
○ **Sunday**

DATE:

ROUTE:

DISTANCE:

TIME:

FUEL

BEFORE:

DURING:

AFTER:

CROSS-TRAINING:

Rate how you felt before the run (1 being the worst and 10 being the best):

1   2   3   4   5   6   7   8   9   10

GOALS AND GOAL CHECK-IN:

_____

_____

_____

_____

_____

_____

_____

_____

_____

_____

_____

Any major obstacles?

Any major accomplishments?

Did you run with anyone? ○ Yes ○ No
 If yes, who?

Rate how you felt after the run (1 being the worst and 10 being the best):

1 2 3 4 5 6 7 8 9 10

OTHER NOTES OR COMMENTS (WEATHER, INJURIES, ETC.):

_____

_____

_____

_____

_____

_____

_____

_____

_____

_____

_____

_____

HALF-MARATHON PLAN

Beginner

MON	TUES	WED	THURS	FRI	SAT	SUN	TOTAL
Rest/XT	2 miles	Rest/XT	6 miles total, with 4 miles @ HMP	2 miles	3 miles	9 miles LSD	22 miles

Intermediate

MON	TUES	WED	THURS	FRI	SAT	SUN	TOTAL
Rest/XT	3 miles	3 miles	6 miles total, with 4 miles @ HMP	3 miles	Rest/XT	11 miles LSD	26 miles

Advanced

MON	TUES	WED	THURS	FRI	SAT	SUN	TOTAL
Rest/XT	6 miles	6 miles	7 miles total, with 5 miles @ HMP	5 miles	5 miles	12 miles LSD	41 miles

Key of running terms appears on last page.

MARATHON PLAN

Beginner

MON	TUES	WED	THURS	FRI	SAT	SUN	TOTAL
Rest	4 miles	Rest	4 miles	Rest	4 miles	15 miles LSD	**27 miles**

Intermediate

MON	TUES	WED	THURS	FRI	SAT	SUN	TOTAL
Rest	6 miles easy with 6 strides	7 miles hills	Rest	5 miles total, with 3 miles @ MP	5 miles easy	16 miles LSD	**39 miles**

Advanced

MON	TUES	WED	THURS	FRI	SAT	SUN	TOTAL
5 miles easy with 5 strides	8 miles hills	5 miles easy	8 miles total, with 6 miles @ MP	Rest	4 miles easy	18 miles LSD	**48 miles**

Key of running terms appears on last page.

- ○ **Monday**
- ○ **Tuesday**
- ○ **Wednesday**
- ○ **Thursday**
- ○ **Friday**
- ○ **Saturday**
- ○ **Sunday**

DATE:

ROUTE:

DISTANCE:

TIME:

FUEL

BEFORE:

DURING:

AFTER:

CROSS-TRAINING:

Rate how you felt before the run (1 being the worst and 10 being the best):

1 2 3 4 5 6 7 8 9 10

GOALS AND GOAL CHECK-IN:

_____

_____

_____

_____

_____

_____

_____

_____

_____

_____

_____

_____

Any major obstacles?

Any major accomplishments?

Did you run with anyone? ○ Yes ○ No

If yes, who?

Rate how you felt after the run (1 being the worst and 10 being the best):

1 2 3 4 5 6 7 8 9 10

OTHER NOTES OR COMMENTS (WEATHER, INJURIES, ETC.):

_____

_____

_____

_____

_____

_____

_____

_____

_____

_____

_____

○ **Monday**
○ **Tuesday**
○ **Wednesday**
○ **Thursday**
○ **Friday**
○ **Saturday**
○ **Sunday**

DATE:

ROUTE:

DISTANCE:

TIME:

FUEL

BEFORE:

DURING:

AFTER:

CROSS-TRAINING:

Rate how you felt before the run (1 being the worst and 10 being the best):

1   2   3   4   5   6   7   8   9   10

GOALS AND GOAL CHECK-IN:

_____
_____
_____
_____
_____
_____
_____
_____
_____
_____
_____
_____

Any major obstacles?

Any major accomplishments?

Did you run with anyone? ○ Yes ○ No

If yes, who?

Rate how you felt after the run (1 being the worst and 10 being the best):

1 2 3 4 5 6 7 8 9 10

OTHER NOTES OR COMMENTS (WEATHER, INJURIES, ETC.):

_____

_____

_____

_____

_____

_____

_____

_____

_____

_____

○ **Monday**
○ **Tuesday**
○ **Wednesday**
○ **Thursday**
○ **Friday**
○ **Saturday**
○ **Sunday**

DATE:

ROUTE:

DISTANCE:

TIME:

FUEL

BEFORE:

DURING:

AFTER:

CROSS-TRAINING:

Rate how you felt before the run (1 being the worst and 10 being the best):

1   2   3   4   5   6   7   8   9   10

GOALS AND GOAL CHECK-IN:

_____

_____

_____

_____

_____

_____

_____

_____

_____

_____

_____

Any major obstacles?

Any major accomplishments?

Did you run with anyone? ○ Yes ○ No

If yes, who?

Rate how you felt after the run (1 being the worst and 10 being the best):

1 2 3 4 5 6 7 8 9 10

OTHER NOTES OR COMMENTS (WEATHER, INJURIES, ETC.):

_____

_____

_____

_____

_____

_____

_____

_____

_____

_____

○ **Monday**
○ **Tuesday**
○ **Wednesday**
○ **Thursday**
○ **Friday**
○ **Saturday**
○ **Sunday**

DATE:

ROUTE:

DISTANCE:

TIME:

FUEL
  BEFORE:
  DURING:
  AFTER:

CROSS-TRAINING:

Rate how you felt before the run (1 being the worst and 10 being the best):

1 2 3 4 5 6 7 8 9 10

GOALS AND GOAL CHECK-IN:

_____

_____

_____

_____

_____

_____

_____

_____

_____

_____

_____

Any major obstacles?

Any major accomplishments?

Did you run with anyone? ○ Yes ○ No
If yes, who?

Rate how you felt after the run (1 being the worst and 10 being the best):

1 2 3 4 5 6 7 8 9 10

OTHER NOTES OR COMMENTS (WEATHER, INJURIES, ETC.):

_____

_____

_____

_____

_____

_____

_____

_____

_____

_____

_____

_____

_____

○ **Monday**

○ **Tuesday**

○ **Wednesday**

○ **Thursday**

○ **Friday**

○ **Saturday**

○ **Sunday**

DATE:

ROUTE:

DISTANCE:

TIME:

FUEL

BEFORE:

DURING:

AFTER:

CROSS-TRAINING:

Rate how you felt before the run (1 being the worst and 10 being the best):

1   2   3   4   5   6   7   8   9   10

GOALS AND GOAL CHECK-IN:

_____

_____

_____

_____

_____

_____

_____

_____

_____

_____

_____

Any major obstacles?

Any major accomplishments?

Did you run with anyone? ○ Yes ○ No
If yes, who?

Rate how you felt after the run (1 being the worst and 10 being the best):

1   2   3   4   5   6   7   8   9   10

OTHER NOTES OR COMMENTS (WEATHER, INJURIES, ETC.):

○ **Monday**
○ **Tuesday**
○ **Wednesday**
○ **Thursday**
○ **Friday**
○ **Saturday**
○ **Sunday**

DATE:

ROUTE:

DISTANCE:

TIME:

FUEL

 BEFORE:

 DURING:

 AFTER:

CROSS-TRAINING:

Rate how you felt before the run (1 being the worst and 10 being the best):

1   2   3   4   5   6   7   8   9   10

GOALS AND GOAL CHECK-IN:

_____

_____

_____

_____

_____

_____

_____

_____

_____

_____

_____

Any major obstacles?

Any major accomplishments?

Did you run with anyone? ○ Yes ○ No
If yes, who?

Rate how you felt after the run (1 being the worst and 10 being the best):

1   2   3   4   5   6   7   8   9   10

OTHER NOTES OR COMMENTS (WEATHER, INJURIES, ETC.):

○ **Monday**

○ **Tuesday**

○ **Wednesday**

○ **Thursday**

○ **Friday**

○ **Saturday**

○ **Sunday**

DATE:

ROUTE:

DISTANCE:

TIME:

FUEL

BEFORE:

DURING:

AFTER:

CROSS-TRAINING:

Rate how you felt before the run (1 being the worst and 10 being the best):

1 2 3 4 5 6 7 8 9 10

GOALS AND GOAL CHECK-IN:

_____

_____

_____

_____

_____

_____

_____

_____

_____

_____

_____

Any major obstacles?

Any major accomplishments?

Did you run with anyone? ○ Yes ○ No
If yes, who?

Rate how you felt after the run (1 being the worst and 10 being the best):

1 2 3 4 5 6 7 8 9 10

OTHER NOTES OR COMMENTS (WEATHER, INJURIES, ETC.):

_____

_____

_____

_____

_____

_____

_____

_____

_____

_____

_____

HALF-MARATHON PLAN

Beginner

MON	TUES	WED	THURS	FRI	SAT	SUN	TOTAL
Rest/XT	2 miles	Rest/XT	6 miles total, with 4 miles @ HMP	2 miles	3 miles	10 miles LSD	**23 miles**

Intermediate

MON	TUES	WED	THURS	FRI	SAT	SUN	TOTAL
Rest/XT	3 miles	3 miles	7 miles total, with 5 miles @ HMP	4 miles	Rest/XT	13 miles LSD	**30 miles**

Advanced

MON	TUES	WED	THURS	FRI	SAT	SUN	TOTAL
Rest/XT	6 miles	6 miles	8 miles total, with 6 miles @ HMP	5 miles	5 miles	13 miles LSD	**43 miles**

Key of running terms appears on last page.

WEEK 8

MARATHON PLAN

Beginner

MON	TUES	WED	THURS	FRI	SAT	SUN	TOTAL
Rest	4 miles	Time trial (1 mile)	4 miles	Rest	4 miles	12 miles LSD or half marathon	**25 miles**

Intermediate

MON	TUES	WED	THURS	FRI	SAT	SUN	TOTAL
Rest	5 miles easy with 5 strides	Hill repeats 8 miles with 8 hill repeats	Rest	Time trial	4 miles easy	14 miles LSD or half marathon	**32 miles**

Advanced

MON	TUES	WED	THURS	FRI	SAT	SUN	TOTAL
5 miles easy with 5 strides	Hill repeats 8 miles with 8 hill repeats	4 miles easy	9 miles total, with 7 miles @ MP	Rest	3 miles easy	13 miles LSD or half marathon	**42 miles**

Key of running terms appears on last page.

○ **Monday**
○ **Tuesday**
○ **Wednesday**
○ **Thursday**
○ **Friday**
○ **Saturday**
○ **Sunday**

DATE:

ROUTE:

DISTANCE:

TIME:

FUEL

BEFORE:

DURING:

AFTER:

CROSS-TRAINING:

Rate how you felt before the run (1 being the worst and 10 being the best):

1 2 3 4 5 6 7 8 9 10

GOALS AND GOAL CHECK-IN:

Any major obstacles?

Any major accomplishments?

Did you run with anyone? ○ Yes ○ No

If yes, who?

Rate how you felt after the run (1 being the worst and 10 being the best):

1 2 3 4 5 6 7 8 9 10

OTHER NOTES OR COMMENTS (WEATHER, INJURIES, ETC.):

_____

_____

_____

_____

_____

_____

_____

_____

_____

_____

_____

_____

○ **Monday**
○ **Tuesday**
○ **Wednesday**
○ **Thursday**
○ **Friday**
○ **Saturday**
○ **Sunday**

DATE:

ROUTE:

DISTANCE:

TIME:

FUEL

BEFORE:

DURING:

AFTER:

CROSS-TRAINING:

Rate how you felt before the run (1 being the worst and 10 being the best):

1   2   3   4   5   6   7   8   9   10

GOALS AND GOAL CHECK-IN:

_____
_____
_____
_____
_____
_____
_____
_____
_____
_____
_____
_____

Any major obstacles?

Any major accomplishments?

Did you run with anyone? ○ Yes ○ No

If yes, who?

Rate how you felt after the run (1 being the worst and 10 being the best):

1 2 3 4 5 6 7 8 9 10

OTHER NOTES OR COMMENTS (WEATHER, INJURIES, ETC.):

○ **Monday**
○ **Tuesday**
○ **Wednesday**
○ **Thursday**
○ **Friday**
○ **Saturday**
○ **Sunday**

DATE:

ROUTE:

DISTANCE:

TIME:

FUEL

BEFORE:

DURING:

AFTER:

CROSS-TRAINING:

Rate how you felt before the run (1 being the worst and 10 being the best):

1   2   3   4   5   6   7   8   9   10

GOALS AND GOAL CHECK-IN:

_____

_____

_____

_____

_____

_____

_____

_____

_____

_____

Any major obstacles?

Any major accomplishments?

Did you run with anyone? ○ Yes ○ No
If yes, who?

Rate how you felt after the run (1 being the worst and 10 being the best):

1 2 3 4 5 6 7 8 9 10

OTHER NOTES OR COMMENTS (WEATHER, INJURIES, ETC.):

_____

_____

_____

_____

_____

_____

_____

_____

_____

_____

_____

○ **Monday**

○ **Tuesday**

○ **Wednesday**

○ **Thursday**

○ **Friday**

○ **Saturday**

○ **Sunday**

DATE:

ROUTE:

DISTANCE:

TIME:

FUEL

  BEFORE:

  DURING:

  AFTER:

CROSS-TRAINING:

Rate how you felt before the run (1 being the worst and 10 being the best):

1 2 3 4 5 6 7 8 9 10

GOALS AND GOAL CHECK-IN:

Any major obstacles?

Any major accomplishments?

Did you run with anyone? ○ Yes ○ No
If yes, who?

Rate how you felt after the run (1 being the worst and 10 being the best):

1 2 3 4 5 6 7 8 9 10

OTHER NOTES OR COMMENTS (WEATHER, INJURIES, ETC.):

_____

_____

_____

_____

_____

_____

_____

_____

_____

_____

_____

○ **Monday**
○ **Tuesday**
○ **Wednesday**
○ **Thursday**
○ **Friday**
○ **Saturday**
○ **Sunday**

DATE:

ROUTE:

DISTANCE:

TIME:

FUEL

BEFORE:

DURING:

AFTER:

CROSS-TRAINING:

Rate how you felt before the run (1 being the worst and 10 being the best):

1   2   3   4   5   6   7   8   9   10

GOALS AND GOAL CHECK-IN:

_____
_____
_____
_____
_____
_____
_____
_____
_____
_____
_____

Any major obstacles?

Any major accomplishments?

Did you run with anyone? ○ Yes ○ No
If yes, who?

Rate how you felt after the run (1 being the worst and 10 being the best):

1 2 3 4 5 6 7 8 9 10

OTHER NOTES OR COMMENTS (WEATHER, INJURIES, ETC.):

_____
_____
_____
_____
_____
_____
_____
_____
_____
_____
_____

○ **Monday**
○ **Tuesday**
○ **Wednesday**
○ **Thursday**
○ **Friday**
○ **Saturday**
○ **Sunday**

DATE:

ROUTE:

DISTANCE:

TIME:

FUEL

BEFORE:

DURING:

AFTER:

CROSS-TRAINING:

Rate how you felt before the run (1 being the worst and 10 being the best):

1 2 3 4 5 6 7 8 9 10

GOALS AND GOAL CHECK-IN:

_____

_____

_____

_____

_____

_____

_____

_____

_____

_____

_____

Any major obstacles?

Any major accomplishments?

Did you run with anyone? ○ Yes ○ No

If yes, who?

Rate how you felt after the run (1 being the worst and 10 being the best):

1 2 3 4 5 6 7 8 9 10

OTHER NOTES OR COMMENTS (WEATHER, INJURIES, ETC.):

_____

_____

_____

_____

_____

_____

_____

_____

_____

_____

_____

○ **Monday**
○ **Tuesday**
○ **Wednesday**
○ **Thursday**
○ **Friday**
○ **Saturday**
○ **Sunday**

DATE:

ROUTE:

DISTANCE:

TIME:

FUEL

BEFORE:

DURING:

AFTER:

CROSS-TRAINING:

Rate how you felt before the run (1 being the worst and 10 being the best):

1   2   3   4   5   6   7   8   9   10

GOALS AND GOAL CHECK-IN:

_____
_____
_____
_____
_____
_____
_____
_____
_____
_____
_____

Any major obstacles?

Any major accomplishments?

Did you run with anyone? ○ Yes ○ No

If yes, who?

Rate how you felt after the run (1 being the worst and 10 being the best):

1 2 3 4 5 6 7 8 9 10

OTHER NOTES OR COMMENTS (WEATHER, INJURIES, ETC.):

_____

_____

_____

_____

_____

_____

_____

_____

_____

_____

_____

HALF-MARATHON PLAN

Beginner

MON	TUES	WED	THURS	FRI	SAT	SUN	TOTAL
Rest/XT	2 miles	Rest/XT	8 miles total, with 6 miles @ HMP	2 miles	2 miles	9 miles LSD	**23 miles**

Intermediate

MON	TUES	WED	THURS	FRI	SAT	SUN	TOTAL
Rest/XT	3 miles	3 miles	Mile repeats 8 miles with 4 x 1 mile	3 miles	Rest/XT	11 miles LSD	**28 miles**

Advanced

MON	TUES	WED	THURS	FRI	SAT	SUN	TOTAL
Rest/XT	6 miles	6 miles	Mile repeats 10 miles with 5 x 1 mile	Rest/XT	5 miles	11 miles LSD	**38 miles**

Key of running terms appears on last page.

MARATHON PLAN

Beginner

MON	TUES	WED	THURS	FRI	SAT	SUN	TOTAL
Rest	4 miles with 4 strides	Rest	6 miles	Rest	4 miles	16 miles LSD	**30 miles**

Intermediate

MON	TUES	WED	THURS	FRI	SAT	SUN	TOTAL
Rest	3 miles easy with 3 strides	Mile repeats 8 miles with 3 x 1 mile	Rest	9 miles total, with 7 miles @ MP	5 miles easy	18 miles LSD, fast finish	**41 miles**

Advanced

MON	TUES	WED	THURS	FRI	SAT	SUN	TOTAL
Rest	5 miles easy with 5 strides	Mile repeats 8 miles with 3 x 1 miles	4 miles easy	9 miles with 8 miles @ MP	5 miles easy	20 miles LSD, fast finish	**51 miles**

Key of running terms appears on last page.

○ **Monday**
○ **Tuesday**
○ **Wednesday**
○ **Thursday**
○ **Friday**
○ **Saturday**
○ **Sunday**

DATE:

ROUTE:

DISTANCE:

TIME:

FUEL

BEFORE:

DURING:

AFTER:

CROSS-TRAINING:

Rate how you felt before the run (1 being the worst and 10 being the best):

1   2   3   4   5   6   7   8   9   10

GOALS AND GOAL CHECK-IN:

_____

_____

_____

_____

_____

_____

_____

_____

_____

_____

_____

Any major obstacles?

Any major accomplishments?

Did you run with anyone? ○ Yes ○ No
If yes, who?

Rate how you felt after the run (1 being the worst and 10 being the best):

1 2 3 4 5 6 7 8 9 10

OTHER NOTES OR COMMENTS (WEATHER, INJURIES, ETC.):

_____

_____

_____

_____

_____

_____

_____

_____

_____

_____

_____

_____

○ **Monday**
○ **Tuesday**
○ **Wednesday**
○ **Thursday**
○ **Friday**
○ **Saturday**
○ **Sunday**

DATE:

ROUTE:

DISTANCE:

TIME:

FUEL

BEFORE:

DURING:

AFTER:

CROSS-TRAINING:

Rate how you felt before the run (1 being the worst and 10 being the best):

1 2 3 4 5 6 7 8 9 10

GOALS AND GOAL CHECK-IN:

_____

_____

_____

_____

_____

_____

_____

_____

_____

_____

_____

Any major obstacles?

Any major accomplishments?

Did you run with anyone? ○ Yes ○ No

If yes, who?

Rate how you felt after the run (1 being the worst and 10 being the best):

1 2 3 4 5 6 7 8 9 10

OTHER NOTES OR COMMENTS (WEATHER, INJURIES, ETC.):

_____

_____

_____

_____

_____

_____

_____

_____

_____

_____

_____

○ **Monday**

○ **Tuesday**

○ **Wednesday**

○ **Thursday**

○ **Friday**

○ **Saturday**

○ **Sunday**

DATE:

ROUTE:

DISTANCE:

TIME:

FUEL

BEFORE:

DURING:

AFTER:

CROSS-TRAINING:

Rate how you felt before the run (1 being the worst and 10 being the best):

1   2   3   4   5   6   7   8   9   10

GOALS AND GOAL CHECK-IN:

_____

_____

_____

_____

_____

_____

_____

_____

_____

_____

_____

Any major obstacles?

Any major accomplishments?

Did you run with anyone? ○ Yes ○ No

If yes, who?

Rate how you felt after the run (1 being the worst and 10 being the best):

1   2   3   4   5   6   7   8   9   10

OTHER NOTES OR COMMENTS (WEATHER, INJURIES, ETC.):

_____

_____

_____

_____

_____

_____

_____

_____

_____

_____

○ **Monday**
○ **Tuesday**
○ **Wednesday**
○ **Thursday**
○ **Friday**
○ **Saturday**
○ **Sunday**

DATE:

ROUTE:

DISTANCE:

TIME:

FUEL

  BEFORE:

  DURING:

  AFTER:

CROSS-TRAINING:

Rate how you felt before the run (1 being the worst and 10 being the best):

1   2   3   4   5   6   7   8   9   10

GOALS AND GOAL CHECK-IN:

Any major obstacles?

Any major accomplishments?

Did you run with anyone? ○ Yes ○ No
If yes, who?

Rate how you felt after the run (1 being the worst and 10 being the best):

1 2 3 4 5 6 7 8 9 10

OTHER NOTES OR COMMENTS (WEATHER, INJURIES, ETC.):

_____

_____

_____

_____

_____

_____

_____

_____

_____

_____

_____

_____

○ **Monday**
○ **Tuesday**
○ **Wednesday**
○ **Thursday**
○ **Friday**
○ **Saturday**
○ **Sunday**

DATE:

ROUTE:

DISTANCE:

TIME:

FUEL

BEFORE:

DURING:

AFTER:

CROSS-TRAINING:

Rate how you felt before the run (1 being the worst and 10 being the best):

1 2 3 4 5 6 7 8 9 10

GOALS AND GOAL CHECK-IN:

_____
_____
_____
_____
_____
_____
_____
_____
_____
_____
_____

Any major obstacles?

Any major accomplishments?

Did you run with anyone? ○ Yes ○ No
If yes, who?

Rate how you felt after the run (1 being the worst and 10 being the best):

1 2 3 4 5 6 7 8 9 10

OTHER NOTES OR COMMENTS (WEATHER, INJURIES, ETC.):

_____

_____

_____

_____

_____

_____

_____

_____

_____

_____

_____

- ○ **Monday**
- ○ **Tuesday**
- ○ **Wednesday**
- ○ **Thursday**
- ○ **Friday**
- ○ **Saturday**
- ○ **Sunday**

DATE:

ROUTE:

DISTANCE:

TIME:

FUEL

  BEFORE:

  DURING:

  AFTER:

CROSS-TRAINING:

Rate how you felt before the run (1 being the worst and 10 being the best):

1 2 3 4 5 6 7 8 9 10

GOALS AND GOAL CHECK-IN:

_____

_____

_____

_____

_____

_____

_____

_____

_____

_____

_____

Any major obstacles?

Any major accomplishments?

Did you run with anyone? ○ Yes ○ No
If yes, who?

Rate how you felt after the run (1 being the worst and 10 being the best):

1 2 3 4 5 6 7 8 9 10

OTHER NOTES OR COMMENTS (WEATHER, INJURIES, ETC.):

○ **Monday**
○ **Tuesday**
○ **Wednesday**
○ **Thursday**
○ **Friday**
○ **Saturday**
○ **Sunday**

DATE:

ROUTE:

DISTANCE:

TIME:

FUEL

BEFORE:

DURING:

AFTER:

CROSS-TRAINING:

Rate how you felt before the run (1 being the worst and 10 being the best):

1 2 3 4 5 6 7 8 9 10

GOALS AND GOAL CHECK-IN:

_____

_____

_____

_____

_____

_____

_____

_____

_____

_____

_____

_____

Any major obstacles?

Any major accomplishments?

Did you run with anyone? ○ Yes ○ No
If yes, who?

Rate how you felt after the run (1 being the worst and 10 being the best):

1   2   3   4   5   6   7   8   9   10

OTHER NOTES OR COMMENTS (WEATHER, INJURIES, ETC.):

_____

_____

_____

_____

_____

_____

_____

_____

_____

_____

HALF-MARATHON PLAN

Beginner

MON	TUES	WED	THURS	FRI	SAT	SUN	TOTAL
Rest/XT	2 miles	Rest/XT	5 miles total, with 3 miles @ HMP	Rest/XT	2 miles	Race day	22.1 miles

Intermediate

MON	TUES	WED	THURS	FRI	SAT	SUN	TOTAL
Rest/XT	3 miles	3 miles	5 miles total, with 3 miles @ HMP	4 miles	Rest/XT	Race day	27.1 miles

Advanced

MON	TUES	WED	THURS	FRI	SAT	SUN	TOTAL
Rest/XT	4 miles	4 miles	6 miles total, with 4 miles @ HMP	4 miles	Rest/XT	Race day	30.1 miles

Key of running terms appears on last page.

MARATHON PLAN

Beginner

MON	TUES	WED	THURS	FRI	SAT	SUN	TOTAL
Rest	4 miles with 4 strides	Rest	6 miles	Rest	4 miles	18 miles LSD	**32 miles**

Intermediate

MON	TUES	WED	THURS	FRI	SAT	SUN	TOTAL
Rest	4 miles easy with 4 strides	Yasso 800s 9 miles with 6 x 800	Rest	10 miles total, with 9 miles @ MP	Rest	20 miles LSD, fast finish	**43 miles**

Advanced

MON	TUES	WED	THURS	FRI	SAT	SUN	TOTAL
4 miles easy	6 miles easy with 6 strides	Yasso 800s 9 miles with 6 x 800	6 miles easy	10 miles total, with 8 miles @ MP	6 miles easy	22 miles LSD, fast finish	**59 miles**

Key of running terms appears on last page.

○ **Monday**
○ **Tuesday**
○ **Wednesday**
○ **Thursday**
○ **Friday**
○ **Saturday**
○ **Sunday**

DATE:

ROUTE:

DISTANCE:

TIME:

FUEL

  BEFORE:

  DURING:

  AFTER:

CROSS-TRAINING:

Rate how you felt before the run (1 being the worst and 10 being the best):

1 2 3 4 5 6 7 8 9 10

GOALS AND GOAL CHECK-IN:

Any major obstacles?

Any major accomplishments?

Did you run with anyone? ○ Yes ○ No
If yes, who?

Rate how you felt after the run (1 being the worst and 10 being the best):

1 2 3 4 5 6 7 8 9 10

OTHER NOTES OR COMMENTS (WEATHER, INJURIES, ETC.):

- ○ **Monday**
- ○ **Tuesday**
- ○ **Wednesday**
- ○ **Thursday**
- ○ **Friday**
- ○ **Saturday**
- ○ **Sunday**

DATE:

ROUTE:

DISTANCE:

TIME:

FUEL

BEFORE:

DURING:

AFTER:

CROSS-TRAINING:

Rate how you felt before the run (1 being the worst and 10 being the best):

1 2 3 4 5 6 7 8 9 10

GOALS AND GOAL CHECK-IN:

_____

_____

_____

_____

_____

_____

_____

_____

_____

_____

_____

Any major obstacles?

Any major accomplishments?

Did you run with anyone? ○ Yes ○ No
If yes, who?

Rate how you felt after the run (1 being the worst and 10 being the best):

1 2 3 4 5 6 7 8 9 10

OTHER NOTES OR COMMENTS (WEATHER, INJURIES, ETC.):

_____

_____

_____

_____

_____

_____

_____

_____

_____

_____

_____

○ **Monday**
○ **Tuesday**
○ **Wednesday**
○ **Thursday**
○ **Friday**
○ **Saturday**
○ **Sunday**

DATE:

ROUTE:

DISTANCE:

TIME:

FUEL

BEFORE:

DURING:

AFTER:

CROSS-TRAINING:

Rate how you felt before the run (1 being the worst and 10 being the best):

1 2 3 4 5 6 7 8 9 10

GOALS AND GOAL CHECK-IN:

_____
_____
_____
_____
_____
_____
_____
_____
_____
_____
_____

Any major obstacles?

Any major accomplishments?

Did you run with anyone? ○ Yes ○ No

If yes, who?

Rate how you felt after the run (1 being the worst and 10 being the best):

1 2 3 4 5 6 7 8 9 10

OTHER NOTES OR COMMENTS (WEATHER, INJURIES, ETC.):

○ **Monday**
○ **Tuesday**
○ **Wednesday**
○ **Thursday**
○ **Friday**
○ **Saturday**
○ **Sunday**

DATE:

ROUTE:

DISTANCE:

TIME:

FUEL

BEFORE:

DURING:

AFTER:

CROSS-TRAINING:

Rate how you felt before the run (1 being the worst and 10 being the best):

1 2 3 4 5 6 7 8 9 10

GOALS AND GOAL CHECK-IN:

_____
_____
_____
_____
_____
_____
_____
_____
_____
_____
_____
_____

Any major obstacles?

Any major accomplishments?

Did you run with anyone? ○ Yes ○ No

If yes, who?

Rate how you felt after the run (1 being the worst and 10 being the best):

1 2 3 4 5 6 7 8 9 10

OTHER NOTES OR COMMENTS (WEATHER, INJURIES, ETC.):

_____

_____

_____

_____

_____

_____

_____

_____

_____

_____

_____

○ **Monday**
○ **Tuesday**
○ **Wednesday**
○ **Thursday**
○ **Friday**
○ **Saturday**
○ **Sunday**

DATE:

ROUTE:

DISTANCE:

TIME:

FUEL
  BEFORE:
  DURING:
  AFTER:

CROSS-TRAINING:

Rate how you felt before the run (1 being the worst and 10 being the best):

1   2   3   4   5   6   7   8   9   10

GOALS AND GOAL CHECK-IN:

_____

_____

_____

_____

_____

_____

_____

_____

_____

_____

Any major obstacles?

Any major accomplishments?

Did you run with anyone? ○ Yes ○ No
If yes, who?

Rate how you felt after the run (1 being the worst and 10 being the best):

1   2   3   4   5   6   7   8   9   10

OTHER NOTES OR COMMENTS (WEATHER, INJURIES, ETC.):

_____

_____

_____

_____

_____

_____

_____

_____

_____

_____

_____

○ **Monday**

○ **Tuesday**

○ **Wednesday**

○ **Thursday**

○ **Friday**

○ **Saturday**

○ **Sunday**

DATE:

ROUTE:

DISTANCE:

TIME:

FUEL

  BEFORE:

  DURING:

  AFTER:

CROSS-TRAINING:

Rate how you felt before the run (1 being the worst and 10 being the best):

1   2   3   4   5   6   7   8   9   10

GOALS AND GOAL CHECK-IN:

_____

_____

_____

_____

_____

_____

_____

_____

_____

_____

_____

Any major obstacles?

Any major accomplishments?

Did you run with anyone? ○ Yes ○ No

If yes, who?

Rate how you felt after the run (1 being the worst and 10 being the best):

1 2 3 4 5 6 7 8 9 10

OTHER NOTES OR COMMENTS (WEATHER, INJURIES, ETC.):

○ Monday

○ Tuesday

○ Wednesday

○ Thursday

○ Friday

○ Saturday

○ Sunday

DATE:

ROUTE:

DISTANCE:

TIME:

FUEL

BEFORE:

DURING:

AFTER:

CROSS-TRAINING:

Rate how you felt before the run (1 being the worst and 10 being the best):

1 2 3 4 5 6 7 8 9 10

GOALS AND GOAL CHECK-IN:

Any major obstacles?

Any major accomplishments?

Did you run with anyone? ○ Yes ○ No
If yes, who?

Rate how you felt after the run (1 being the worst and 10 being the best):

1 2 3 4 5 6 7 8 9 10

OTHER NOTES OR COMMENTS (WEATHER, INJURIES, ETC.):

_____

_____

_____

_____

_____

_____

_____

_____

_____

_____

_____

MARATHON PLAN

Beginner

MON	TUES	WED	THURS	FRI	SAT	SUN	TOTAL
Rest	6 miles with 6 strides	Rest	5 miles	Rest	5 miles	20 miles LSD	**36 miles**

Intermediate

MON	TUES	WED	THURS	FRI	SAT	SUN	TOTAL
Rest	4 miles easy with 4 strides	7 miles easy	Rest	10 miles total, with 8 miles @ MP	4 miles easy	20 miles LSD, fast finish	**45 miles**

Advanced

MON	TUES	WED	THURS	FRI	SAT	SUN	TOTAL
Rest	8 miles easy with 8 strides	Yasso 800s 9 miles with 6 x 800	7 miles easy	8 miles total, with 6 miles @ MP	6 miles easy	22 miles LSD, fast finish	**60 miles**

Key of running terms appears on last page.

- ○ **Monday**
- ○ **Tuesday**
- ○ **Wednesday**
- ○ **Thursday**
- ○ **Friday**
- ○ **Saturday**
- ○ **Sunday**

DATE:

ROUTE:

DISTANCE:

TIME:

FUEL

BEFORE:

DURING:

AFTER:

CROSS-TRAINING:

Rate how you felt before the run (1 being the worst and 10 being the best):

1   2   3   4   5   6   7   8   9   10

Rate how you felt after the run (1 being the worst and 10 being the best):

1   2   3   4   5   6   7   8   9   10

OTHER NOTES OR COMMENTS (WEATHER, INJURIES, ETC.):

_____

_____

_____

_____

_____

_____

_____

○ **Monday**

○ **Tuesday**

○ **Wednesday**

○ **Thursday**

○ **Friday**

○ **Saturday**

○ **Sunday**

DATE:

ROUTE:

DISTANCE:

TIME:

FUEL

BEFORE:

DURING:

AFTER:

CROSS-TRAINING:

Rate how you felt before the run (1 being the worst and 10 being the best):

1 2 3 4 5 6 7 8 9 10

Rate how you felt after the run (1 being the worst and 10 being the best):

1 2 3 4 5 6 7 8 9 10

OTHER NOTES OR COMMENTS (WEATHER, INJURIES, ETC.):

○ **Monday**
○ **Tuesday**
○ **Wednesday**
○ **Thursday**
○ **Friday**
○ **Saturday**
○ **Sunday**

DATE:

ROUTE:

DISTANCE:

TIME:

FUEL

BEFORE:

DURING:

AFTER:

CROSS-TRAINING:

Rate how you felt before the run (1 being the worst and 10 being the best):

1   2   3   4   5   6   7   8   9   10

Rate how you felt after the run (1 being the worst and 10 being the best):

1   2   3   4   5   6   7   8   9   10

OTHER NOTES OR COMMENTS (WEATHER, INJURIES, ETC.):

_____

_____

_____

_____

_____

_____

_____

○ **Monday**
○ **Tuesday**
○ **Wednesday**
○ **Thursday**
○ **Friday**
○ **Saturday**
○ **Sunday**

DATE:

ROUTE:

DISTANCE:

TIME:

FUEL

BEFORE:

DURING:

AFTER:

CROSS-TRAINING:

Rate how you felt before the run (1 being the worst and 10 being the best):

1   2   3   4   5   6   7   8   9   10

Rate how you felt after the run (1 being the worst and 10 being the best):

1   2   3   4   5   6   7   8   9   10

OTHER NOTES OR COMMENTS (WEATHER, INJURIES, ETC.):

_____
_____
_____
_____
_____
_____
_____

○ Monday
○ Tuesday
○ Wednesday
○ Thursday
○ Friday
○ Saturday
○ Sunday

DATE:

ROUTE:

DISTANCE:

TIME:

FUEL

BEFORE:

DURING:

AFTER:

CROSS-TRAINING:

Rate how you felt before the run (1 being the worst and 10 being the best):

1   2   3   4   5   6   7   8   9   10

Rate how you felt after the run (1 being the worst and 10 being the best):

1   2   3   4   5   6   7   8   9   10

OTHER NOTES OR COMMENTS (WEATHER, INJURIES, ETC.):

_____
_____
_____
_____
_____
_____
_____

○ **Monday**
○ **Tuesday**
○ **Wednesday**
○ **Thursday**
○ **Friday**
○ **Saturday**
○ **Sunday**

DATE:

ROUTE:

DISTANCE:

TIME:

FUEL

BEFORE:

DURING:

AFTER:

CROSS-TRAINING:

Rate how you felt before the run (1 being the worst and 10 being the best):

1 2 3 4 5 6 7 8 9 10

Rate how you felt after the run (1 being the worst and 10 being the best):

1 2 3 4 5 6 7 8 9 10

OTHER NOTES OR COMMENTS (WEATHER, INJURIES, ETC.):

_____

_____

_____

_____

_____

_____

_____

○ **Monday**
○ **Tuesday**
○ **Wednesday**
○ **Thursday**
○ **Friday**
○ **Saturday**
○ **Sunday**

DATE:

ROUTE:

DISTANCE:

TIME:

FUEL

 BEFORE:

 DURING:

 AFTER:

CROSS-TRAINING:

Rate how you felt before the run (1 being the worst and 10 being the best):

1 2 3 4 5 6 7 8 9 10

Rate how you felt after the run (1 being the worst and 10 being the best):

1 2 3 4 5 6 7 8 9 10

OTHER NOTES OR COMMENTS (WEATHER, INJURIES, ETC.):

_____

_____

_____

_____

_____

_____

_____

_____

MARATHON PLAN

Beginner

MON	TUES	WED	THURS	FRI	SAT	SUN	TOTAL
Rest	7 miles with 7 strides	Time trial (1 mile)	7 miles	Rest	7 miles	14 miles LSD	**36 miles**

Intermediate

MON	TUES	WED	THURS	FRI	SAT	SUN	TOTAL
Rest	Time trial	Mile repeats 9 miles with 4 x 1 mile	6 miles easy	7 miles total, with 5 miles @ MP	8 miles easy	15 miles LSD	**46 miles**

Advanced

MON	TUES	WED	THURS	FRI	SAT	SUN	TOTAL
Rest	6 miles easy with 6 strides	Mile repeats 9 miles with 4 x 1 mile	7 miles easy	10 miles total, with 8 miles @ MP	8 miles easy	14 miles LSD, fast finish	**54 miles**

Key of running terms appears on last page.

○ **Monday**
○ **Tuesday**
○ **Wednesday**
○ **Thursday**
○ **Friday**
○ **Saturday**
○ **Sunday**

DATE:

ROUTE:

DISTANCE:

TIME:

FUEL

BEFORE:

DURING:

AFTER:

CROSS-TRAINING:

Rate how you felt before the run (1 being the worst and 10 being the best):

1   2   3   4   5   6   7   8   9   10

Rate how you felt after the run (1 being the worst and 10 being the best):

1   2   3   4   5   6   7   8   9   10

OTHER NOTES OR COMMENTS (WEATHER, INJURIES, ETC.):

_____

_____

_____

_____

_____

_____

_____

○ **Monday**
○ **Tuesday**
○ **Wednesday**
○ **Thursday**
○ **Friday**
○ **Saturday**
○ **Sunday**

DATE:

ROUTE:

DISTANCE:

TIME:

FUEL

  BEFORE:

  DURING:

  AFTER:

CROSS-TRAINING:

Rate how you felt before the run (1 being the worst and 10 being the best):

1 2 3 4 5 6 7 8 9 10

Rate how you felt after the run (1 being the worst and 10 being the best):

1 2 3 4 5 6 7 8 9 10

OTHER NOTES OR COMMENTS (WEATHER, INJURIES, ETC.):

_____

_____

_____

_____

_____

_____

_____

○ **Monday**
○ **Tuesday**
○ **Wednesday**
○ **Thursday**
○ **Friday**
○ **Saturday**
○ **Sunday**

DATE:

ROUTE:

DISTANCE:

TIME:

FUEL
  BEFORE:
  DURING:
  AFTER:

CROSS-TRAINING:

Rate how you felt before the run (1 being the worst and 10 being the best):

1   2   3   4   5   6   7   8   9   10

Rate how you felt after the run (1 being the worst and 10 being the best):

1   2   3   4   5   6   7   8   9   10

OTHER NOTES OR COMMENTS (WEATHER, INJURIES, ETC.):

_____

_____

_____

_____

_____

_____

_____

_____

WEEK 12 DAY 4

○ **Monday**
○ **Tuesday**
○ **Wednesday**
○ **Thursday**
○ **Friday**
○ **Saturday**
○ **Sunday**

DATE:

ROUTE:

DISTANCE:

TIME:

FUEL

BEFORE:

DURING:

AFTER:

CROSS-TRAINING:

Rate how you felt before the run (1 being the worst and 10 being the best):

1 2 3 4 5 6 7 8 9 10

Rate how you felt after the run (1 being the worst and 10 being the best):

1 2 3 4 5 6 7 8 9 10

OTHER NOTES OR COMMENTS (WEATHER, INJURIES, ETC.):

○ **Monday**
○ **Tuesday**
○ **Wednesday**
○ **Thursday**
○ **Friday**
○ **Saturday**
○ **Sunday**

DATE:

ROUTE:

DISTANCE:

TIME:

FUEL

BEFORE:

DURING:

AFTER:

CROSS-TRAINING:

Rate how you felt before the run (1 being the worst and 10 being the best):

1 2 3 4 5 6 7 8 9 10

Rate how you felt after the run (1 being the worst and 10 being the best):

1 2 3 4 5 6 7 8 9 10

OTHER NOTES OR COMMENTS (WEATHER, INJURIES, ETC.):

_____

_____

_____

_____

_____

_____

_____

○ **Monday**
○ **Tuesday**
○ **Wednesday**
○ **Thursday**
○ **Friday**
○ **Saturday**
○ **Sunday**

DATE:

ROUTE:

DISTANCE:

TIME:

FUEL

 BEFORE:

 DURING:

 AFTER:

CROSS-TRAINING:

Rate how you felt before the run (1 being the worst and 10 being the best):

1 2 3 4 5 6 7 8 9 10

Rate how you felt after the run (1 being the worst and 10 being the best):

1 2 3 4 5 6 7 8 9 10

OTHER NOTES OR COMMENTS (WEATHER, INJURIES, ETC.):

_____
_____
_____
_____
_____
_____
_____

- ○ **Monday**
- ○ **Tuesday**
- ○ **Wednesday**
- ○ **Thursday**
- ○ **Friday**
- ○ **Saturday**
- ○ **Sunday**

DATE:

ROUTE:

DISTANCE:

TIME:

FUEL

BEFORE:

DURING:

AFTER:

CROSS-TRAINING:

Rate how you felt before the run (1 being the worst and 10 being the best):

1 2 3 4 5 6 7 8 9 10

Rate how you felt after the run (1 being the worst and 10 being the best):

1 2 3 4 5 6 7 8 9 10

OTHER NOTES OR COMMENTS (WEATHER, INJURIES, ETC.):

MARATHON PLAN

Beginner

MON	TUES	WED	THURS	FRI	SAT	SUN	TOTAL
Rest	6 miles with 6 strides	Rest	7 miles	Rest	7 miles	20 miles LSD	**40 miles**

Intermediate

MON	TUES	WED	THURS	FRI	SAT	SUN	TOTAL
Rest	6 miles easy with 6 strides	Yasso 800s 10 miles with 8 x 800	Rest	6 miles easy	6 miles easy	22 miles LSD	**50 miles**

Advanced

MON	TUES	WED	THURS	FRI	SAT	SUN	TOTAL
Rest	6 miles easy with 6 strides	Yasso 800s 10 miles with 8 x 800	7 miles easy	8 miles hills	6 miles easy	23 miles LSD, fast finish	**53 miles**

Key of running terms appears on last page.

○ **Monday**
○ **Tuesday**
○ **Wednesday**
○ **Thursday**
○ **Friday**
○ **Saturday**
○ **Sunday**

DATE:

ROUTE:

DISTANCE:

TIME:

FUEL

BEFORE:

DURING:

AFTER:

CROSS-TRAINING:

Rate how you felt before the run (1 being the worst and 10 being the best):

1 2 3 4 5 6 7 8 9 10

Rate how you felt after the run (1 being the worst and 10 being the best):

1 2 3 4 5 6 7 8 9 10

OTHER NOTES OR COMMENTS (WEATHER, INJURIES, ETC.):

_____

_____

_____

_____

_____

_____

_____

○ **Monday**
○ **Tuesday**
○ **Wednesday**
○ **Thursday**
○ **Friday**
○ **Saturday**
○ **Sunday**

DATE:

ROUTE:

DISTANCE:

TIME:

FUEL

BEFORE:

DURING:

AFTER:

CROSS-TRAINING:

Rate how you felt before the run (1 being the worst and 10 being the best):

1 2 3 4 5 6 7 8 9 10

Rate how you felt after the run (1 being the worst and 10 being the best):

1 2 3 4 5 6 7 8 9 10

OTHER NOTES OR COMMENTS (WEATHER, INJURIES, ETC.):

- ○ **Monday**
- ○ **Tuesday**
- ○ **Wednesday**
- ○ **Thursday**
- ○ **Friday**
- ○ **Saturday**
- ○ **Sunday**

DATE:

ROUTE:

DISTANCE:

TIME:

FUEL

BEFORE:

DURING:

AFTER:

CROSS-TRAINING:

Rate how you felt before the run (1 being the worst and 10 being the best):

1   2   3   4   5   6   7   8   9   10

Rate how you felt after the run (1 being the worst and 10 being the best):

1   2   3   4   5   6   7   8   9   10

OTHER NOTES OR COMMENTS (WEATHER, INJURIES, ETC.):

○ **Monday**
○ **Tuesday**
○ **Wednesday**
○ **Thursday**
○ **Friday**
○ **Saturday**
○ **Sunday**

DATE:

ROUTE:

DISTANCE:

TIME:

FUEL

BEFORE:

DURING:

AFTER:

CROSS-TRAINING:

Rate how you felt before the run (1 being the worst and 10 being the best):

1 2 3 4 5 6 7 8 9 10

Rate how you felt after the run (1 being the worst and 10 being the best):

1 2 3 4 5 6 7 8 9 10

OTHER NOTES OR COMMENTS (WEATHER, INJURIES, ETC.):

_____
_____
_____
_____
_____
_____
_____

- ○ **Monday**
- ○ **Tuesday**
- ○ **Wednesday**
- ○ **Thursday**
- ○ **Friday**
- ○ **Saturday**
- ○ **Sunday**

DATE:

ROUTE:

DISTANCE:

TIME:

FUEL

BEFORE:

DURING:

AFTER:

CROSS-TRAINING:

Rate how you felt before the run (1 being the worst and 10 being the best):

1 2 3 4 5 6 7 8 9 10

Rate how you felt after the run (1 being the worst and 10 being the best):

1 2 3 4 5 6 7 8 9 10

OTHER NOTES OR COMMENTS (WEATHER, INJURIES, ETC.):

_____

_____

_____

_____

_____

_____

_____

- ○ **Monday**
- ○ **Tuesday**
- ○ **Wednesday**
- ○ **Thursday**
- ○ **Friday**
- ○ **Saturday**
- ○ **Sunday**

DATE:

ROUTE:

DISTANCE:

TIME:

FUEL

BEFORE:

DURING:

AFTER:

CROSS-TRAINING:

Rate how you felt before the run (1 being the worst and 10 being the best):

1 2 3 4 5 6 7 8 9 10

Rate how you felt after the run (1 being the worst and 10 being the best):

1 2 3 4 5 6 7 8 9 10

OTHER NOTES OR COMMENTS (WEATHER, INJURIES, ETC.):

_____

_____

_____

_____

_____

_____

_____

○ **Monday**

○ **Tuesday**

○ **Wednesday**

○ **Thursday**

○ **Friday**

○ **Saturday**

○ **Sunday**

DATE:

ROUTE:

DISTANCE:

TIME:

FUEL

  BEFORE:

  DURING:

  AFTER:

CROSS-TRAINING:

Rate how you felt before the run (1 being the worst and 10 being the best):

1   2   3   4   5   6   7   8   9   10

Rate how you felt after the run (1 being the worst and 10 being the best):

1   2   3   4   5   6   7   8   9   10

OTHER NOTES OR COMMENTS (WEATHER, INJURIES, ETC.):

_____

_____

_____

_____

_____

_____

_____

_____

MARATHON PLAN

Beginner

MON	TUES	WED	THURS	FRI	SAT	SUN	TOTAL
Rest	7 miles with 7 strides	Rest	7 miles	Rest	7 miles	13 miles LSD	**34 miles**

Intermediate

MON	TUES	WED	THURS	FRI	SAT	SUN	TOTAL
Rest	8 miles easy with 8 strides	Mile repeats 8 miles with 3 x 1 mile	Rest	7 miles easy	6 miles easy	15 miles LSD or half marathon	**45 miles**

Advanced

MON	TUES	WED	THURS	FRI	SAT	SUN	TOTAL
Rest	7 miles easy with 7 strides	Mile repeats 8 miles with 3 x 1 mile	6 miles easy	10 miles total, with 9 miles @ MP	6 miles easy	16 miles LSD, fast finish	**53 miles**

Key of running terms appears on last page.

○ **Monday**
○ **Tuesday**
○ **Wednesday**
○ **Thursday**
○ **Friday**
○ **Saturday**
○ **Sunday**

DATE:

ROUTE:

DISTANCE:

TIME:

FUEL
 BEFORE:
 DURING:
 AFTER:

CROSS-TRAINING:

Rate how you felt before the run (1 being the worst and 10 being the best):

1 2 3 4 5 6 7 8 9 10

Rate how you felt after the run (1 being the worst and 10 being the best):

1 2 3 4 5 6 7 8 9 10

OTHER NOTES OR COMMENTS (WEATHER, INJURIES, ETC.):

_____
_____
_____
_____
_____
_____
_____
_____

○ **Monday**
○ **Tuesday**
○ **Wednesday**
○ **Thursday**
○ **Friday**
○ **Saturday**
○ **Sunday**

DATE:

ROUTE:

DISTANCE:

TIME:

FUEL

BEFORE:

DURING:

AFTER:

CROSS-TRAINING:

Rate how you felt before the run (1 being the worst and 10 being the best):

1   2   3   4   5   6   7   8   9   10

Rate how you felt after the run (1 being the worst and 10 being the best):

1   2   3   4   5   6   7   8   9   10

OTHER NOTES OR COMMENTS (WEATHER, INJURIES, ETC.):

_____

_____

_____

_____

_____

_____

_____

○ **Monday**

○ **Tuesday**

○ **Wednesday**

○ **Thursday**

○ **Friday**

○ **Saturday**

○ **Sunday**

DATE:

ROUTE:

DISTANCE:

TIME:

FUEL

  BEFORE:

  DURING:

  AFTER:

CROSS-TRAINING:

Rate how you felt before the run (1 being the worst and 10 being the best):

1   2   3   4   5   6   7   8   9   10

Rate how you felt after the run (1 being the worst and 10 being the best):

1   2   3   4   5   6   7   8   9   10

OTHER NOTES OR COMMENTS (WEATHER, INJURIES, ETC.):

_____

_____

_____

_____

_____

_____

_____

○ **Monday**

○ **Tuesday**

○ **Wednesday**

○ **Thursday**

○ **Friday**

○ **Saturday**

○ **Sunday**

DATE:

ROUTE:

DISTANCE:

TIME:

FUEL

BEFORE:

DURING:

AFTER:

CROSS-TRAINING:

Rate how you felt before the run (1 being the worst and 10 being the best):

1   2   3   4   5   6   7   8   9   10

Rate how you felt after the run (1 being the worst and 10 being the best):

1   2   3   4   5   6   7   8   9   10

OTHER NOTES OR COMMENTS (WEATHER, INJURIES, ETC.):

○ **Monday**
○ **Tuesday**
○ **Wednesday**
○ **Thursday**
○ **Friday**
○ **Saturday**
○ **Sunday**

DATE:

ROUTE:

DISTANCE:

TIME:

FUEL
  BEFORE:
  DURING:
  AFTER:

CROSS-TRAINING:

Rate how you felt before the run (1 being the worst and 10 being the best):

1   2   3   4   5   6   7   8   9   10

Rate how you felt after the run (1 being the worst and 10 being the best):

1   2   3   4   5   6   7   8   9   10

OTHER NOTES OR COMMENTS (WEATHER, INJURIES, ETC.):

_____

_____

_____

_____

_____

_____

_____

○ **Monday**
○ **Tuesday**
○ **Wednesday**
○ **Thursday**
○ **Friday**
○ **Saturday**
○ **Sunday**

DATE:

ROUTE:

DISTANCE:

TIME:

FUEL

BEFORE:

DURING:

AFTER:

CROSS-TRAINING:

Rate how you felt before the run (1 being the worst and 10 being the best):

1   2   3   4   5   6   7   8   9   10

Rate how you felt after the run (1 being the worst and 10 being the best):

1   2   3   4   5   6   7   8   9   10

OTHER NOTES OR COMMENTS (WEATHER, INJURIES, ETC.):

_____

_____

_____

_____

_____

_____

_____

○ **Monday**
○ **Tuesday**
○ **Wednesday**
○ **Thursday**
○ **Friday**
○ **Saturday**
○ **Sunday**

DATE:

ROUTE:

DISTANCE:

TIME:

FUEL

  BEFORE:

  DURING:

  AFTER:

CROSS-TRAINING:

Rate how you felt before the run (1 being the worst and 10 being the best):

1   2   3   4   5   6   7   8   9   10

Rate how you felt after the run (1 being the worst and 10 being the best):

1   2   3   4   5   6   7   8   9   10

OTHER NOTES OR COMMENTS (WEATHER, INJURIES, ETC.):

MARATHON PLAN

Beginner

MON	TUES	WED	THURS	FRI	SAT	SUN	TOTAL
Rest	5 miles with 5 strides	Rest	4 miles	Rest	5 miles	10 miles LSD	**24 miles**

Intermediate

MON	TUES	WED	THURS	FRI	SAT	SUN	TOTAL
Rest	5 miles easy with 5 strides	4 miles easy	Rest	6 miles easy	5 miles easy	12 miles LSD	**32 miles**

Advanced

MON	TUES	WED	THURS	FRI	SAT	SUN	TOTAL
Rest	4 miles easy with 4 strides	7 miles hills	4 miles easy	8 miles total, with 6 miles @ MP	6 miles easy	13 miles LSD	**40 miles**

Key of running terms appears on last page.

○ **Monday**
○ **Tuesday**
○ **Wednesday**
○ **Thursday**
○ **Friday**
○ **Saturday**
○ **Sunday**

DATE:

ROUTE:

DISTANCE:

TIME:

FUEL

BEFORE:

DURING:

AFTER:

CROSS-TRAINING:

Rate how you felt before the run (1 being the worst and 10 being the best):

1   2   3   4   5   6   7   8   9   10

Rate how you felt after the run (1 being the worst and 10 being the best):

1   2   3   4   5   6   7   8   9   10

OTHER NOTES OR COMMENTS (WEATHER, INJURIES, ETC.):

_____

_____

_____

_____

_____

_____

_____

○ **Monday**

○ **Tuesday**

○ **Wednesday**

○ **Thursday**

○ **Friday**

○ **Saturday**

○ **Sunday**

DATE:

ROUTE:

DISTANCE:

TIME:

FUEL

BEFORE:

DURING:

AFTER:

CROSS-TRAINING:

Rate how you felt before the run (1 being the worst and 10 being the best):

1 2 3 4 5 6 7 8 9 10

Rate how you felt after the run (1 being the worst and 10 being the best):

1 2 3 4 5 6 7 8 9 10

OTHER NOTES OR COMMENTS (WEATHER, INJURIES, ETC.):

_____

_____

_____

_____

_____

_____

_____

○ **Monday**
○ **Tuesday**
○ **Wednesday**
○ **Thursday**
○ **Friday**
○ **Saturday**
○ **Sunday**

DATE:

ROUTE:

DISTANCE:

TIME:

FUEL
BEFORE:
DURING:
AFTER:

CROSS-TRAINING:

Rate how you felt before the run (1 being the worst and 10 being the best):

1   2   3   4   5   6   7   8   9   10

Rate how you felt after the run (1 being the worst and 10 being the best):

1   2   3   4   5   6   7   8   9   10

OTHER NOTES OR COMMENTS (WEATHER, INJURIES, ETC.):

_____

_____

_____

_____

_____

_____

_____

○ **Monday**
○ **Tuesday**
○ **Wednesday**
○ **Thursday**
○ **Friday**
○ **Saturday**
○ **Sunday**

DATE:

ROUTE:

DISTANCE:

TIME:

FUEL

BEFORE:

DURING:

AFTER:

CROSS-TRAINING:

Rate how you felt before the run (1 being the worst and 10 being the best):

1 2 3 4 5 6 7 8 9 10

Rate how you felt after the run (1 being the worst and 10 being the best):

1 2 3 4 5 6 7 8 9 10

OTHER NOTES OR COMMENTS (WEATHER, INJURIES, ETC.):

○ **Monday**
○ **Tuesday**
○ **Wednesday**
○ **Thursday**
○ **Friday**
○ **Saturday**
○ **Sunday**

DATE:
ROUTE:
DISTANCE:
TIME:
FUEL
 BEFORE:
 DURING:
 AFTER:
CROSS-TRAINING:

Rate how you felt before the run (1 being the worst and 10 being the best):

1 2 3 4 5 6 7 8 9 10

Rate how you felt after the run (1 being the worst and 10 being the best):

1 2 3 4 5 6 7 8 9 10

OTHER NOTES OR COMMENTS (WEATHER, INJURIES, ETC.):

_____
_____
_____
_____
_____
_____
_____
_____

○ **Monday**
○ **Tuesday**
○ **Wednesday**
○ **Thursday**
○ **Friday**
○ **Saturday**
○ **Sunday**

DATE:

ROUTE:

DISTANCE:

TIME:

FUEL

BEFORE:

DURING:

AFTER:

CROSS-TRAINING:

Rate how you felt before the run (1 being the worst and 10 being the best):

1   2   3   4   5   6   7   8   9   10

Rate how you felt after the run (1 being the worst and 10 being the best):

1   2   3   4   5   6   7   8   9   10

OTHER NOTES OR COMMENTS (WEATHER, INJURIES, ETC.):

_____

_____

_____

_____

_____

_____

_____

○ **Monday**
○ **Tuesday**
○ **Wednesday**
○ **Thursday**
○ **Friday**
○ **Saturday**
○ **Sunday**

DATE:

ROUTE:

DISTANCE:

TIME:

FUEL

 BEFORE:

 DURING:

 AFTER:

CROSS-TRAINING:

Rate how you felt before the run (1 being the worst and 10 being the best):

1 2 3 4 5 6 7 8 9 10

Rate how you felt after the run (1 being the worst and 10 being the best):

1 2 3 4 5 6 7 8 9 10

OTHER NOTES OR COMMENTS (WEATHER, INJURIES, ETC.):

_____

_____

_____

_____

_____

_____

_____

_____

WEEK 16
MARATHON PLAN

Beginner

MON	TUES	WED	THURS	FRI	SAT	SUN	TOTAL
Rest	3 miles	Time trial (1 mile)	4 miles	Rest	3 miles	Race day	37.2 miles

Intermediate

MON	TUES	WED	THURS	FRI	SAT	SUN	TOTAL
Rest	Time trial	Rest	5 miles easy	Rest	3 miles very easy	Race day	35.2 miles

Advanced

MON	TUES	WED	THURS	FRI	SAT	SUN	TOTAL
Rest	5 miles easy with 5 strides	Rest	3 miles easy	Rest	3 miles very easy	Race day	37.2 miles

Key of running terms appears on last page.

○ **Monday**

○ **Tuesday**

○ **Wednesday**

○ **Thursday**

○ **Friday**

○ **Saturday**

○ **Sunday**

DATE:

ROUTE:

DISTANCE:

TIME:

FUEL

BEFORE:

DURING:

AFTER:

CROSS-TRAINING:

Rate how you felt before the run (1 being the worst and 10 being the best):

1   2   3   4   5   6   7   8   9   10

Rate how you felt after the run (1 being the worst and 10 being the best):

1   2   3   4   5   6   7   8   9   10

OTHER NOTES OR COMMENTS (WEATHER, INJURIES, ETC.):

_____

_____

_____

_____

_____

_____

_____

○ **Monday**
○ **Tuesday**
○ **Wednesday**
○ **Thursday**
○ **Friday**
○ **Saturday**
○ **Sunday**

DATE:

ROUTE:

DISTANCE:

TIME:

FUEL

BEFORE:

DURING:

AFTER:

CROSS-TRAINING:

Rate how you felt before the run (1 being the worst and 10 being the best):

1 2 3 4 5 6 7 8 9 10

Rate how you felt after the run (1 being the worst and 10 being the best):

1 2 3 4 5 6 7 8 9 10

OTHER NOTES OR COMMENTS (WEATHER, INJURIES, ETC.):

_____
_____
_____
_____
_____
_____
_____
_____

○ **Monday**
○ **Tuesday**
○ **Wednesday**
○ **Thursday**
○ **Friday**
○ **Saturday**
○ **Sunday**

DATE:

ROUTE:

DISTANCE:

TIME:

FUEL

BEFORE:

DURING:

AFTER:

CROSS-TRAINING:

Rate how you felt before the run (1 being the worst and 10 being the best):

1   2   3   4   5   6   7   8   9   10

Rate how you felt after the run (1 being the worst and 10 being the best):

1   2   3   4   5   6   7   8   9   10

OTHER NOTES OR COMMENTS (WEATHER, INJURIES, ETC.):

_____

_____

_____

_____

_____

_____

_____

○ **Monday**
○ **Tuesday**
○ **Wednesday**
○ **Thursday**
○ **Friday**
○ **Saturday**
○ **Sunday**

DATE:

ROUTE:

DISTANCE:

TIME:

FUEL

BEFORE:

DURING:

AFTER:

CROSS-TRAINING:

Rate how you felt before the run (1 being the worst and 10 being the best):

1 2 3 4 5 6 7 8 9 10

Rate how you felt after the run (1 being the worst and 10 being the best):

1 2 3 4 5 6 7 8 9 10

OTHER NOTES OR COMMENTS (WEATHER, INJURIES, ETC.):

_____

_____

_____

_____

_____

_____

_____

○ **Monday**
○ **Tuesday**
○ **Wednesday**
○ **Thursday**
○ **Friday**
○ **Saturday**
○ **Sunday**

DATE:

ROUTE:

DISTANCE:

TIME:

FUEL

BEFORE:

DURING:

AFTER:

CROSS-TRAINING:

Rate how you felt before the run (1 being the worst and 10 being the best):

1 2 3 4 5 6 7 8 9 10

Rate how you felt after the run (1 being the worst and 10 being the best):

1 2 3 4 5 6 7 8 9 10

OTHER NOTES OR COMMENTS (WEATHER, INJURIES, ETC.):

_____

_____

_____

_____

_____

_____

_____

○ **Monday**
○ **Tuesday**
○ **Wednesday**
○ **Thursday**
○ **Friday**
○ **Saturday**
○ **Sunday**

DATE:

ROUTE:

DISTANCE:

TIME:

FUEL

BEFORE:

DURING:

AFTER:

CROSS-TRAINING:

Rate how you felt before the run (1 being the worst and 10 being the best):

1   2   3   4   5   6   7   8   9   10

Rate how you felt after the run (1 being the worst and 10 being the best):

1   2   3   4   5   6   7   8   9   10

OTHER NOTES OR COMMENTS (WEATHER, INJURIES, ETC.):

_____

_____

_____

_____

_____

_____

_____

○ **Monday**
○ **Tuesday**
○ **Wednesday**
○ **Thursday**
○ **Friday**
○ **Saturday**
○ **Sunday**

DATE:

ROUTE:

DISTANCE:

TIME:

FUEL

BEFORE:

DURING:

AFTER:

CROSS-TRAINING:

Rate how you felt before the run (1 being the worst and 10 being the best):

1 2 3 4 5 6 7 8 9 10

Rate how you felt after the run (1 being the worst and 10 being the best):

1 2 3 4 5 6 7 8 9 10

OTHER NOTES OR COMMENTS (WEATHER, INJURIES, ETC.):

Key

EASY: Run at a comfortable, conversational pace. These are interchangeable with rest days. You can cross-train on an easy day instead with a sustained aerobic effort on a bike or the elliptical trainer for the same amount of time you'd spend running.

HILL REPEATS: Find a hill that will take you at least 2 minutes to climb, and mark off a "short" repeat halfway from the bottom and a "long" repeat at the top. After a 2-mile warmup, run up to the short mark three or four times, jogging back down to recover in between. Then run up to the top three or four times, jogging back down to the short mark and then sprinting to the bottom. (Try to maintain smooth form, without slapping your feet.) Finish with three or four sprints up to the short mark. Cool down with 2 miles of easy running. The total mileage for the day will amount to about 8 miles.

HILLS: Run the mileage for the day on the hilliest course you can find. Hills build a base of strength during the first 7 weeks of the program.

HMP: Half-marathon pace. This is the pace that you hope to maintain during the race. To figure out your half-marathon pace, you can do a 1-mile time trial. Go to a 400-meter track or any stretch of road that's 1 mile long. After a 10-minute warmup, time yourself while running four laps (1 mile) as fast as you can. Cool down with 10 minutes of walking and jogging. Plug that time into the training calculator at runnersworld.com to find out what a realistic half-marathon time and pace should be.

LSD: This is a long slow distance run to build endurance. LSDs should be done at an easy, conversational pace, 1 to 2 minutes slower than your goal marathon pace. Later on you can practice a fast finish by picking up the pace for the last 2 to 3 miles.

MILE REPEATS: Warm up with 2 miles of easy running. Run a mile at your 10-K pace, jog 400 meters for recovery, and repeat that cycle as directed. Cool down with 2 two miles of easy running.

MP: Marathon goal pace. Practice the speed you're hoping to hit in the race. Run 1 mile easy for a warmup and 1 mile easy for a cooldown.

REST: Take a rest day, or do moderate cross-training with a no-impact activity like yoga or swimming.

REST/XT: Take a rest day, or do moderate cross-training with a no-impact activity like yoga or swimming.

STRIDES: Adding strides to any easy run activates fast-twitch muscle fibers, improves coordination and leg turnover, and preps your body for the race. Near the end of your run, gradually accelerate over 100 meters until you reach 90 percent of all-out effort. Hold that effort for 5 seconds, then smoothly decelerate. Walk to recover between each stride. The exact distance of each stride is not critical.

YASSO 800s: Warm up with 2 miles of easy running, then run 800 meters at a time that's "equal" to your marathon time. That is, if you're shooting for a 4:10 marathon, try to run each 800-meter repeat in 4 minutes and 10 seconds. Jog 400 meters in between the 800s. Cool down with 2 miles of easy running.